SCHOLASTIC

NO FUSS

SCIENCE
PHOTOCOPIABLES
AGES 7-11

LEVELS

3-5

- Levelled and linked to the curriculum

- Stand-alone photocopiable activities

- Ideal for mixed-age classes

Compiled by Roger Smith

C000320045

CONTRIBUTORS

Text © **Catherine Musto and Marion Cranmer**: 15, 16, 29, 30, 34, 35, 42, 43, 46, 54, 62, 63, 75, 76, 77, 78, 84, 90, 94, 95, 96

Text © **John Davis and Sonia Tibbatts**: 26, 27, 28, 44, 45, 53, 55, 56, 57, 58, 91, 92, 93

Text © **Rose Griffiths**: 17, 18, 19, 20, 31, 32, 33, 41, 47, 48, 49, 50, 51, 52, 59, 60, 61, 64, 65, 66, 67, 68, 69, 70

Text © **Leonie McKinnon**: 81, 82, 83, 87, 88, 89, 97, 98, 99, 101, 102, 104, 105, 106, 109, 110, 111, 112, 113, 114, 115, 116, 117, 118, 119, 120, 121, 122, 123, 124, 125, 126, 127

Text © **Barbara Raper**: 21, 22, 23, 24, 25, 36, 37, 38, 39, 40, 71, 72, 73, 74, 79, 80, 85, 86, 100, 103, 107, 108

CONSULTANT EDITOR

Roger Smith

ASSISTANT EDITOR

Wendy Tse

DESIGNERS

Lapiz Digital

COVER DESIGN

Anna Oliwa

ILLUSTRATORS

Illustration © **Caroline Ewen**: 97, 98, 99, 101, 102, 104, 105, 106, 109, 110, 111, 112, 113, 114, 115, 116, 117, 118, 119, 120, 121, 122, 123, 124, 125, 126, 127

Illustration © **Louise Gardner**: 81, 82, 83, 87, 88, 89

Illustration © **Gloria**: 16, 29, 30, 35, 42, 43, 46, 54, 62, 63, 75, 76, 77, 95, 96

Illustration © **Sarah Hedley**: 31, 32, 47, 64, 65, 100, 103, 107, 108

Illustration © **Helen Herbert**: 33, 85, 86

Illustration © **Kim Lane**: 59, 60, 61, 66, 67, 68, 69, 70, 71, 72, 73, 74, 79, 80

Illustration © **Mary Lonsdale**: 17, 18, 19, 20, 21, 22, 23, 24, 25, 36, 37, 38, 39, 40, 41, 48, 49, 50, 51, 52

Illustration © **Hilary McElderry**: 15, 34, 78, 84, 90, 94

Illustration © **Liz Thomas**: 26, 27, 44, 53, 55, 57, 58, 92, 93

Text and illustration copyright in individual pages as per acknowledgements. Compilation © 2006 Scholastic Ltd

Every effort has been made to trace all the copyright owners of material but there were a few cases where an author or illustrator was untraceable. Scholastic will be happy to correct any omissions in future printings.

Published by Scholastic Ltd
Villiers House
Clarendon Avenue
Leamington Spa
Warwickshire
CV32 5PR

www.scholastic.co.uk

Designed using Adobe InDesign

Printed by Bell & Bain Ltd, Glasgow

4 5 6 7 8 9   7 8 9 0 1 2 3 4 5

British Library Cataloguing-in-Publication Data

A catalogue record for this book is available from the British Library.

ISBN 0-439-96550-0

ISBN 978-0439-96550-7

Extracts from the National Numeracy Strategy reproduced under the terms of HMSO Guidance Note 8. © Crown copyright.

Reproduction of coins by permission of The Royal Mint © Crown copyright.

Photocopiable pages and original teachers' notes first published in *Surveys*, *First fractions*, *First number patterns*, *Measuring*, *Money*, *Numbers to 20*, *Numbers to 50* and *Shapes and patterns* (all first published 1993) from the Essentials for Maths series, and *Exploring shape and space* (1996), *Maths* (1992), *Maths puzzles* (1994) and *Measurement skills* (1996) from the Teacher Timesavers series.

All rights reserved. This book is sold subject to the condition that it shall not, by way of trade or otherwise, be lent, hired out or otherwise circulated without the publisher's prior consent in any form of binding or cover other than that in which it is published and without a similar condition, including this condition, being imposed upon the subsequent purchaser.

No part of this publication may be reproduced, stored in a retrieval system, or transmitted, in any form or by any means, electronic, mechanical, photocopying, recording or otherwise, without the prior permission of the publisher. This book remains copyright, although permission is granted to copy pages where indicated for classroom distribution and use only in the school which has purchased the book, or by the teacher who has purchased the book, and in accordance with the CLA licensing agreement. Photocopying permission is given only for purchasers and not for borrowers of books from any lending service.

SCHOLASTIC
www.scholastic.co.uk

CONTENTS

CONTENTS

INTRODUCTION

If children in the later stages of primary education are to learn science successfully, it needs to be interesting and exciting and it is in the *doing* of the science that they will learn best. This does not just mean practical activities. Each child needs to be encouraged to observe, record, predict, measure, look for patterns, classify, explain and ask questions that lead to further investigations.

The activities in this book are linked to the QCA Scheme of Work for Science, the Programme of Study for Science in the National Curriculum for England and the Scottish 5-14 National Guidelines. While this book does not contain everything that a busy teacher needs, it does provide a wide range of exciting material that has been graded for the appropriate levels of attainment. However, this doesn't mean that if an activity is judged to be Level 3 or C it cannot be completed by children with different ability levels. Each teacher will be able to modify, expand or simplify the activities for mixed-ability classes.

The activities are also flexible. Most can stand alone and illustrate specific objectives, or can be part of a series of lessons. In whatever way they are used, the children will need time to discuss their work before and after the activity, which will help the teacher monitor each child's progress and build on this knowledge when setting future objectives.

The activities can also be adapted to suit different styles of teaching. Some will be useful as homework or for children to plan and complete their own investigations. They can help support and develop a scientific vocabulary and can, because some need to be completed by following precise teacher instructions, promote structured ways of scientific enquiry. Where extra care is necessary it has been indicated in the teaching notes for each activity sheet.

There are no references to Sc1 (Scientific enquiry) in the Programme of Study for Science or the 'Skills in science – investigating' section in the Scottish 5-14 National Guidelines in any of the activities. This is because it is assumed that this is the basis of all science for children at this stage of their development. The wide range of photocopiable activities will mean that teachers who are not specialist science teachers will be able to encourage planning, obtaining and presenting evidence, and considering evidence and evaluating it; these are the key aspects of scientific enquiry and investigating.

As the children use the activity sheets and the everyday items of equipment and materials, they will be able to carry out some quite sophisticated and systematic investigations. The activities will excite children and make them want to discover more and more about how their complex world works – this is one of the most important and rewarding aspects of teaching science.

Page	Activity	Objective	Teachers' notes	QCA Scheme of Work and National Curriculum links	Scottish Curriculum links	KS2 Levels
page 15	Food for your meals	To recognise and understand that some foods are healthier than others and that some foods will damage teeth.	Some initial discussion of healthy and unhealthy food, especially related to sugar, will be useful. To focus the children on the foods we eat (and also what we should and should not eat), ask them to keep a diary of food eaten during the last 24 hours.	QCA Unit 3A 'Teeth and eating'. Builds on Unit 1A 'Ourselves' and 2A 'Health and growth'. NC Sc2 (1) Life processes; (2) Humans and other animals.	Environmental Studies: Society, Science and Technology [ES] Energy and forces: Conversion and transfer of energy – Level C	AT2 Level 2/3
page 16	A closer look at your food	To understand where 'nourishment' in food comes from.	Some initial discussion of foods types such as carbohydrate, protein, fat and vitamins and minerals will be useful. Talk about the relevant quantities of the types of food that should be eaten, and what happens if too much fatty or sugary food is eaten.	QCA Unit 3A 'Teeth and eating'. Builds on Unit 1A 'Ourselves' and 2A 'Health and growth'. NC Sc2 (1) Life processes; (2) Humans and other animals.	ES Energy and forces: Conversion and transfer of energy – Level C	AT2 Level 2/3
page 17	Food for action and growth	To begin to recognise the range of foods that are needed for healthy living.	Food packets (such as cereals and biscuits), tins (such as beans and fish) and cheese and milk labels need to be collected. Use the labels to look for other nutrient words, such as fats, vitamins and minerals. Compare quantities of these nutrients for different types of food.	QCA Unit 3A 'Teeth and eating'. Builds on Unit 1A 'Ourselves' and 2A 'Health and growth'. NC Sc2 (1) Life processes; (2) Humans and other animals.	ES Energy and forces: Conversion and transfer of energy – Level C	AT2 Level 2/3
page 18	Food for warmth and health	To recognise foods that provide fats and vitamins and minerals in different quantities.	The display of food packets can be used to determine foods with high fat content as well as those containing useful vitamins and minerals.	QCA Unit 3A 'Teeth and eating'. Builds on Unit 1A 'Ourselves' and 2A 'Health and growth'. NC Sc2 (1) Life processes; (2) Humans and other animals.	ES Energy and forces: Conversion and transfer of energy – Level C	AT2 Level 2/3
page 19	Teeth and dental care	To learn that humans have teeth that are different shapes and that are used for different purposes.	Children should be asked about how they look after their teeth, how often they go to the dentist and whether they know how many fillings they have.	QCA Unit 3A 'Teeth and eating'. Builds on Unit 1A 'Ourselves' and 2A 'Health and growth'. NC Sc2 (1) Life processes; (2) Humans and other animals.	ES Energy and forces: Conversion and transfer of energy – Level C	AT2 Level 3
page 20	What do plants need?	To find out what plants need to grow strong and healthy. To use results to draw conclusions.	It is important to discuss what plants need so that they can grow properly before this activity to try and find out what the children think will happen. This experiment may take several weeks to complete, and the children may need to devise additional record sheets that could include drawn observations. After the experiment, ask the children to use their results to produce a guide to caring for plants. Develop this experiment by trying different seed types, and outdoor and indoor conditions.	QCA Unit 3B 'Helping plants grow well'. Builds on Unit 1B 'Growing plants' and Unit 2B 'Plants and animals in the local environment'. NC Sc2 (3) Green plants; (5) Living things in their environment.	ES Living things and the processes of life. The processes of life – Level C	AT2 Level 3
page 21	Can seeds grow any way up?	To understand that shoots grow upwards, and roots downwards. To decide what evidence is needed before conclusions can be reached.	Children will have to look closely at the broad bean seeds so that they can recognise which way up they need to be planted for their experiment. It is best to soak the seeds the day before this experiment. They should observe the directions in which the roots and shoots grow, and what they look like.	QCA Unit 3B 'Helping plants grow well'. Builds on Unit 1B 'Growing plants' and Unit 2B 'Plants and animals in the local environment'. NC Sc2 (3) Green plants; (5) Living things in their environment.	ES Living things and the processes of life. The processes of life – Level C	AT2 Level 3
page 22	How plants change	To recognise that plants need healthy roots, leaves and stems to grow well.	Children should complete the sheet before doing the experiment so that they can test whether they decided on the correct sequence. The children should recognise that most of the flowers will eventually die on the plant, but that more bean pods will grow on it.	QCA Unit 3B 'Helping plants grow well'. Builds on Unit 1B 'Growing plants' and Unit 2B 'Plants and animals in the local environment'. NC Sc2 (3) Green plants; (5) Living things in their environment.	ES Living things and the processes of life. The processes of life – Level C	AT2 Level 3
page 23	Bean seedlings	To make careful observations. To make comparisons and draw conclusions.	This sheet summarises some of the objectives of previous sheets but the final experiment should be completed with a variety of different seeds. Possible answers to questions: 1 Nadeem and Paul were investigating the effects of temperature and amount of light on seed germination and plant growth. 2 The seed in the fridge may germinate, but it will not grow due to the low temperature and lack of sunlight. 3 Seeds do not need sunlight to germinate but young seedlings need it to grow strong because the green pigment chlorophyll is only made in sunlight. 4 Green plants need sunlight (as well as water, carbon dioxide and chlorophyll) to make their own food.	QCA Unit 3B 'Helping plants grow well'. Builds on Unit 1B 'Growing plants' and Unit 2B 'Plants and animals in the local environment'. NC Sc2 (3) Green plants; (5) Living things in their environment.	ES Living things and the processes of life. The processes of life – Level C	AT2 Level 3
page 24	Materials all around	To investigate the range of materials in and around their school. To develop appropriate vocabulary to describe the materials.	Children should understand the names of different materials and should be able to conduct simple surveys on their own or with a partner. Try to identify the materials by touch alone. Is it easier to identify materials while blindfolded? Why are some materials recognisable?	QCA Unit 3C 'Characteristics of materials'. Builds on Unit 1C 'Sorting and using materials' and 2D 'Grouping and changing materials'. NC Sc3 (1) Grouping and classifying materials.	ES Earth and space: Materials from Earth – Level C	AT3 Level 3
page 25	Marvellous metals	To know that metals have specific characteristics that determine their uses.	The metal objects that are needed will have to be collected in the days before this sheet is used. Although metals have common properties, there can be differences. Metals are hard, shiny, strong and often seem heavy; they normally feel cold, can be pulled and bent without easily breaking, can be beaten into flat sheets and make a ringing noise when tapped; they conduct electricity and some demonstrate magnetic behaviour.	QCA Unit 3C 'Characteristics of materials'. Builds on Unit 1C 'Sorting and using materials' and 2D 'Grouping and changing materials'. NC Sc3 (1) Grouping and classifying materials.	ES Earth and space: Materials from Earth – Level C	AT3 Level 3
page 26	Wonderful wood	To recognise what needs to be considered when a material is chosen for a particular use.	The collection of pieces of wood needs to be extensive and available before this sheet is used. Wood is widely used, but it can rot and splinter outdoors as a result of weathering. Many animals and plants will live and feed on wood.	QCA Unit 3C 'Characteristics of materials'. Builds on Unit 1C 'Sorting and using materials' and 2D 'Grouping and changing materials'. NC Sc3 (1) Grouping and classifying materials.	ES Earth and space: Materials from Earth – Level C	AT3 Level 3
page 27	Useful plastic	To describe the characteristics of a material. To recognise that plastic has diverse properties, but is difficult to recycle and dispose of.	Many different types of plastics are derived from oil, but the different types cannot be mixed because they are made from different molecule arrangements. This makes plastic difficult to recycle. It is necessary to sort different types of plastic before it is recycled into pellet form. It is important to recycle plastic because it is difficult to dispose of. However, this also means that plastic is a durable and useful material. If the final section of this sheet is completed an area of the school grounds that won't be disturbed needs to be identified.	QCA Unit 3C 'Characteristics of materials'. Builds on Unit 1C 'Sorting and using materials' and 2D 'Grouping and changing materials'. NC Sc3 (1) Grouping and classifying materials.	ES Earth and space: Materials from Earth – Level C	AT3 Level 3

NO FUSS

SCHOLASTIC
www.scholastic.co.uk

Page	Activity	Objective	Teachers' notes	QCA Scheme of Work and National Curriculum links	Scottish Curriculum links	KS2 Levels
page 28	Collecting rocks	To recognise that there are different kinds of rocks with different characteristics.	If it will be difficult to collect different rocks from the local environment, there will need to be a collection of different types available in the classroom.	QCA Unit 3D 'Rocks and soils'. Builds on Unit 1C 'Sorting and using materials' and Unit 2D 'Grouping and changing materials'. NC Sc3 (2) Changing materials.	ES Earth and space: Changing materials – Level C	AT3 Level 3
page 29	Comparing rocks	To compare rocks and develop tests that are fair. To develop a vocabulary that identifies the characteristics of materials.	The same collection of rocks from the previous activity can be used. Safety note: If possible, hold the rock samples in a vice when carrying out the 'scratch test'. Ideally, the children should wear goggles and stout gloves when comparing the strength of rocks.	QCA Unit 3D 'Rocks and soils'. Builds on Unit 1C 'Sorting and using materials' and Unit 2D 'Grouping and changing materials'. NC Sc3 (2) Changing materials.	ES Earth and space: Changing materials – Level C	AT3 Level 3
page 30	What does soil consist of?	To develop a fair test and suggest explanations for conclusions reached. To recognise that soil consists of different proportions of stones, sand, clay and humus.	The heaviest particles of soil will settle first at the bottom of the jar. The lighter particles settle out, in order of size, later. The particles of humus float on the surface of the water. If the last part of this sheet is completed you will need access to different types of soil collected from children's gardens rather than just from the school.	QCA Unit 3D 'Rocks and soils'. Builds on Unit 1C 'Sorting and using materials' and Unit 2D 'Grouping and changing materials'. NC Sc 3 (2) Changing materials.	ES Earth and space: Changing materials – Level C	AT3 Level 3
page 31	Make a model mountain	To complete a test, reach conclusions and begin to explain them. To understand that rivers alter the landscape by eroding material from the surface over which they flow.	The softer materials will erode first as the running water carves V-shaped valleys in the mud. The material eroded will be deposited where the rate of water flow decreases on flat or gently sloping surfaces. This could be done on large boards in the classroom. If possible, it would be better and more spectacular to use an outside area where the construction could be left for others to view.	QCA Unit 3D 'Rocks and soils'. Builds on Unit 1C 'Sorting and using materials' and Unit 2D 'Grouping and changing materials'. NC Sc3 (2) Changing materials.	ES Earth and space: Changing materials – Level C	AT3 Level 3
page 32	Changes in the landscape	To understand that rock is beneath the surface of all landscapes and that human activity changes the landscape.	You might want to develop a local walk when the children are completing the last part of this activity to look at local landscape features. Answers: 1 Water erosion: water wears away at the weaker rocks forming cracks and holes. These enlarge into caves, which in turn eventually form an arch. A stack is formed when the roof of the arch collapses. 2 Wind and water: in deserts, water comes from torrential downpours which causes very step canyons. Plateaux wear away into mesas, then buttes. Sand dunes are caused by the winds. 3 Ice erosion: the gradual, more even wearing away of the glacier forms a rounded valley. Harder rock forms ridges, lakes and waterfalls.	QCA Unit 3D 'Rocks and soils'. Builds on Unit 1C 'Sorting and using materials' and Unit 2D 'Grouping and changing materials'. NC Sc3 (2) Changing materials.	ES Earth and space: Changing materials – Level C	AT3 Level 3
page 33	Making a magnet	To begin to recognise that magnetism is a force that has direction.	This is a short and simple activity but the magnet that is made can be used for other activities and experiments. When a soft iron nail is stroked by a magnet, the iron nail itself becomes a weak magnet. The magnetism is quickly lost once the nail is banged.	QCA Unit 3E 'Magnets and springs'. Builds on Unit 1C 'Sorting and using materials', Unit 1E 'Pushes and pulls' and Unit 2E 'Forces and movement'. NC Sc4 (2) Forces and motion.	ES Energy and forces: Forces and their effects – Level B	AT4 Level 2/3
page 34	Magnetic forces	To understand that only some metals are magnetic. To recognise that like poles of magnets repel, opposite poles attract.	It is important to encourage the children to make predictions before they complete the activity. The materials that are needed will have to be collected before they do the tests. Magnets attract iron, nickel, cobalt and most types of steel. Only the nail, pin and paper-clip are likely to be attracted to the magnet.	QCA Unit 3E 'Magnets and springs'. Builds on Unit 1C 'Sorting and using materials', Unit 1E 'Pushes and pulls' and Unit 2E 'Forces and movement'. NC Sc4 (2) Forces and motion.	ES Energy and forces: Forces and their effects – Level B	AT4 Level 3
page 35	How strong is a magnet?	To observe that magnets have varying strengths. To interpret evidence and use it to draw conclusions and to make accurate measurements.	Magnets of different sizes will be needed. The stronger a magnet is, the more paper-clips it can pick up. This experiment can be developed by testing through how many sheets of paper different magnets will attract a paper-clip.	QCA Unit 3E 'Magnets and springs'. Builds on Unit 1C 'Sorting and using materials', Unit 1E 'Pushes and pulls' and Unit 2E 'Forces and movement'. NC Sc4 (2) Forces and motion.	ES Energy and forces: Forces and their effects – Level B	AT4 Level 3
page 36	Cotton reel crawler	To begin to understand that an elastic band can exert a force and that the force acts in a particular direction. To identify a pattern of results.	This can be used as a Design and technology activity. It requires a collection of material and some simple tools. Discuss the fact that a candle slice or bead reduces friction.	QCA Unit 3E 'Magnets and springs'. Builds on Unit 1C 'Sorting and using materials', Unit 1E 'Pushes and pulls' and Unit 2E 'Forces and movement'. NC Sc4 (2) Forces and motion.	ES Energy and forces: Forces and their effects – Level C	AT4 Level 3
page 37	What causes night and day?	To understand that changes in night and day are caused by Earth's rotation on its axis.	Mark the UK on the globe. Rotate the globe and note its position when it is dawn, day, dusk and night in the UK. Visually impaired children will need specific support in this activity. A darkened room needs to be available.	QCA Unit 3F 'Light and shadows'. Builds on Unit 1D 'Light and dark'. NC Sc4 (3) Light and sound; (4) The Earth and beyond.	ES Energy and forces: Properties and uses of energy – Level C/D ES Earth and space – Level C/D	AT4 Level 3/4
page 38	What colour is sunlight?	To understand that sunlight is a mixture of colours.	A band consisting of the colours of the rainbow will be formed on the wall or ceiling. If the surface of the water is rippled, the colours will recombine to form white light. Children need to be supervised closely and warned about the dangers of looking at the Sun and to not reflect the light into anyone's eyes.	QCA Unit 3F 'Light and shadows'. Builds on Unit 1D 'Light and dark'. NC Sc4 (3) Light and sound; (4) The Earth and beyond.	ES Energy and forces: Properties and uses of energy – Level C/D ES Earth and space: Earth in space – Level C/D	AT4 Level 3/4
page 39	Tracking shadows	To recognise that shadows are formed when objects block light from the Sun and that their position changes over the course of a day.	You will need a sunny day when children can record their observations at regular intervals throughout the day. To extend ideas developed with this activity, discuss why shadows are not always visible indoors.	QCA Unit 3F 'Light and shadows'. Builds on Unit 1D 'Light and dark'. NC Sc4 (3) Light and sound; (4) The Earth and beyond.	ES Energy and forces: Properties and uses of energy – Level C	AT4 Level 3
page 40	Shadows	To make and record more complicated observations of shadows. To consider the position of the Sun at different times of the day.	This is a more complicated series of observations. Before completing this sheet, the children should observe the shadow of one object outdoors at different times of the day to see how the length and shape may change with the position of the Sun.	QCA Unit 3F 'Light and shadows'. Builds on Unit 1D 'Light and dark'. NC Sc4 (3) Light and sound; (4) The Earth and beyond.	ES Energy and forces: Properties and uses of energy – Level C	AT4 Level 3

Page	Activity	Objective	Teachers' notes	QCA Scheme of Work and National Curriculum links	Scottish Curriculum links	KS2 Levels
page 41	The skeleton	To know the scientific vocabulary for some parts of their body.	It will be useful to talk about many of the names for the bones in the human body before completing this activity. Reference materials relating the medical terms for different bones will be needed. Answers: Scapula (shoulder blade); sternum (breast bone); humerus (upper arm); vertebra (spinal column); radius (lower arm); phalanges (fingers); patella (knee cap); tibia (lower leg); fibula (lower leg); metatarsal (feet); cranium (skull); clavicle (collar bone); rib; ulna (lower arm); pelvis (hip); femur (thigh). There are 206 bones in the body.	QCA Unit 4A 'Moving and growing'. Builds on Unit 2A 'Health and growth' and Unit 3A 'Teeth and eating'. NC Sc2 (2) Humans and other animals.	ES Living things and the processes of life: The processes of life – Level C/D	AT2 Level 3/4
page 42	The joints	To understand that parts of the skeleton have to move by a system of joints and muscles.	It will be useful to identify movement using joints (by moving your hips, for example) before this practical activity.	QCA Unit 4A 'Moving and growing'. Builds on Unit 2A 'Health and growth' and Unit 3A 'Teeth and eating'. NC Sc2 (2) Humans and other animals.	ES Living things and the processes of life: The processes of life – Level C/D	AT2 Level 3/4
page 43	The muscles	To understand that parts of the skeleton have to move by a system of joints and muscles.	It will be useful to identify movement using muscles such as arm movements (like flexing your arms to point out the muscles used) before this practical activity.	QCA Unit 4A 'Moving and growing'. Builds on Unit 2A 'Health and growth' and Unit 3A 'Teeth and eating'. NC Sc2 (2) Humans and other animals.	ES Living things and the processes of life: The processes of life – Level C/D	AT2 Level 3/4
page 44	Hands	To use precise measures and make observations, measurements and comparisons.	This activity needs careful supervision to check that the children are being accurate in their observations and measurements. The children should count that there are 15 joints in the fingers and thumb.	QCA Unit 4A 'Moving and growing'. Builds on Unit 2A 'Health and growth' and Unit 3A 'Teeth and eating'. NC Sc2 (2) Humans and other animals.	ES Living things and the processes of life: The processes of life – Level C	AT2 Level 3
page 45	Minibeast sampling	To identify some local habitats and the animals which live in them. To make observations and comparisons.	Reference materials need to be available to identify the creatures. It is important that children know to return the creatures to exactly where they found them.	QCA Unit 4B 'Habitats'. Builds on Unit 2B 'Plants and animals' in the local Environment and Unit 3B 'Helping plants grow well'. NC Sc2 (4) Variation and classification; (5) Living things in their environment.	ES Living things and the processes of life: Interaction of living things with their environment – Level C	AT2 Level 3
page 46	Pond survey	To develop the idea that animals are suited to the environment in which they are found. To observe that different animals are found in different habitats.	This builds on the previous activity and needs much more preparation and accuracy. Access to a thriving pond is essential and knowing what some of the creatures look like is important. Likely observations from the activity: surface dwellers – pond skater, pond snail, water boatman, water beetle; bottom dwellers – dragonfly nymph, freshwater shrimp. Some animals will be found in several areas in the pond, especially good swimmers such as beetles.	QCA Unit 4B 'Habitats'. Builds on Unit 2B 'Plants and animals' in the local Environment and Unit 3B 'Helping plants grow well'. NC Sc1 (4) Variation and classification; (5) Living things in their environment.	ES Living things and the processes of life: Interaction of living things with their environment – Level C	AT2 Level 3
page 47	Plant habitats	To identify specific habitats [a meadow and a wood]. To be able to recognise and compare local plants.	Some work on identifying types of plants and a collection of reference materials will be useful. A camera would also be useful if there is not enough time to make detailed sketches.	QCA Unit 4B 'Habitats'. Builds on Unit 2B 'Plants and animals' in the local Environment and Unit 3B 'Helping plants grow well'. NC Sc2 (4) Variation and classification; (5) Living things in their environment.	ES Living things and the processes of life: Interaction of living things with their environment – Level C/D	AT2 Level 3/4
page 48	What is there living under cover?	To begin to group animals according to their features and to observe the conditions in a very specific habitat.	Children should be able to complete a tally chart before they complete this activity. The middle section can be modified, with column headings for the different locations. A 'wild area', partially covered by stones, bricks, logs, plants and leaves, could be set up in the school grounds for this kind of observational study.	QCA Unit 4B 'Habitats'. Builds on Unit 2B 'Plants and animals' in the local Environment and Unit 3B 'Helping plants grow well'. NC Sc1 (4) Variation and classification; (5) Living things in their environment.	ES Living things and the processes of life: Interaction of living things with their environment – Level C/D	AT2 Level 3/4
page 49	Using pitfall traps	To make reliable observations of organisms and design an appropriate experiment.	You will need a grassy or wooded area of the school grounds that will not be disturbed. Reference materials for identifying species are essential. Before this activity is carried out, discuss what kind of animals the children would expect to see in the school grounds.	QCA Unit 4B 'Habitats'. Builds on Unit 2B 'Plants and animals' in the local Environment and Unit 3B 'Helping plants grow well'. NC Sc2 (4) Variation and classification; (5) Living things in their environment.	ES Living things and the processes of life: Interaction of living things with their environment – Level C/D	AT2 Level 3/4
page 50	Thermometers and temperature	To understand that temperature is a measure of how hot or cold it is, and we use thermometers to measure temperature. To use thermometers correctly.	Practice taking and recording temperatures before completing this activity. The temperature is one aspect of the weather which changes from day to day, and from season to season. Even over a short period of time, temperature will fluctuate quite widely. Safety note: a wall thermometer is easier for children to handle. Where possible, use spirit-filled thermometers.	QCA Unit 4C 'Keeping warm'. Builds on Unit 2D 'Grouping and changing materials' and Unit 3C 'Characteristics of materials'. NC Sc3 (1) Grouping and classifying materials; (2) Changing materials.	ES Earth and space: Changing materials – Level C	AT3 Level 3
page 51	Warming water with the Sun	To recognise that the Sun's energy can be used to heat things up. To understand that black and dark colours absorb the Sun's heat, whereas white and light colours reflect it.	It will be useful to predict what will happen during this activity and then to discuss the results. The water in the jar covered with black paper will be at a higher temperature than that in the jar covered with white paper. Extend this activity by considering the fabrics and fibres used for clothing in hot and cold climates. What colour of clothing would be best in a hot country?	QCA Unit 4C 'Keeping warm'. Builds on Unit 2D 'Grouping and changing materials' and Unit 3C 'Characteristics of materials'. NC Sc3 (1) Grouping and classifying materials; (2) Changing materials.	ES Earth and space: Changing materials – Level C	AT3 Level 3
page 52	Travelling heat	To understand which materials are good at conducting heat.	You will need to have a good collection of materials before starting this activity and access to a freezer as well as a warm/hot place. If a material is a good conductor of heat, the molecules of which it is made up vibrate vigorously as they become heated, and heat is passed from one to the next very quickly. In a bad conductor (good insulator) of heat, the molecules only vibrate a little and do not pass the heat. Metals are good conductors of heat. Cork and polystyrene are good insulators.	QCA Unit 4C 'Keeping warm'. Builds on Unit 2D 'Grouping and changing materials' and Unit 3C 'Characteristics of materials'. NC Sc3 (1) Grouping and classifying materials; (2) Changing materials.	ES Earth and space: Changing materials – Level C/D	AT3 Level 3/4

NO FUSS

SCHOLASTIC
www.scholastic.co.uk

Page	Activity	Objective	Teachers' notes	QCA Scheme of Work and National Curriculum links	Scottish Curriculum links	KS2 Levels
page 53	Keeping cool, staying warm	To understand that good thermal insulators can keep heat out as well as in. To turn ideas about how to insulate things into a form that can be investigated.	It will be useful to discuss predictions before doing this activity. The ice cube which remains unwrapped will melt more quickly than those which have been thermally insulated; the tea cosy will help the liquid to retain its heat longer. Safety note: It is important to take care when using hot water.	QCA Unit 4C 'Keeping warm'. Builds on Unit 2D 'Grouping and changing materials' and Unit 3C 'Characteristics of materials'. NC Sc3 (1) Grouping and classifying materials; (2) Changing materials.	ES Earth and space: Changing materials – Level C/D	AT3 Level 3/4
page 54	Cooling a hot drink	To record results in a table and use the results to draw conclusions	Develop the activity by trying this experiment in the classroom. Take care about using a hot liquid. It is not essential to use hot chocolate – in fact some children could use tea, some coffee, and so on, and then look carefully at the differences [if any] in the results.	QCA Unit 4C 'Keeping warm'. Builds on Unit 2D 'Grouping and changing materials' and Unit 3C 'Characteristics of materials'. NC Sc3 (1) Grouping and classifying materials; (2) Changing materials.	ES Earth and space: Changing materials – Level C/D	AT3 Level 3/4
page 55	Dissolving things	To recognise that changes occur when some solids are added to water.	Children will need to understand what 'dissolving' means before they complete this sheet. Not all substances dissolve in water and some only partly dissolve. Heating increases the rate of dissolving. Fine powders dissolve more quickly than coarse granules. Water is called the solvent and the substance dissolved is called the solute. Solvent + solute = solution. Likely results from the experiment: sugar and salt will dissolve; pepper, flour and scouring powder will not dissolve; bicarbonate of soda will partially dissolve.	QCA Unit 4D 'Solids, liquids and how they can be separated'. Builds on Unit 2D 'Grouping and changing materials', Unit 3C 'Characteristics of materials' and Unit 3D 'Rocks and soils'. NC Sc3 (3) Separating mixtures of materials.	ES Earth and space: Changing materials – Level C/D	AT3 Level 3/4
page 56	Changing colours	To identify changes that occur when substances are mixed together and to explain the conclusions reached.	It is important to make sure that the children are encouraged to predict before they actually complete each section of the sheet. Different (secondary) colours can be made using three primary colours – red, yellow and blue. White light is made up of all the colours of the rainbow. We see an object as being a certain colour because that colour is reflected by the object. In a spinning disc, your eyes are deceived because they cannot pick out the separate colours. If the disc were painted the seven colours of the rainbow, it would look white when spun.	QCA Unit 4D 'Solids, liquids and how they can be separated'. Builds on Unit 2D 'Grouping and changing materials', Unit 3C 'Characteristics of materials' and Unit 3D 'Rocks and soils'. NC Sc3 (3) Separating mixtures of materials.	ES Earth and space: Changing materials – Level C/D	AT3 Level 3/4
page 57	Solids, liquids and gases	To recognise the differences between solids, liquids and gases and to be familiar with them in their immediate environment.	An explanation and discussion of the three states (solid, liquid and gas) would be useful before starting this sheet. The molecules in solids stay in one position, which is why solids can maintain a definite shape. The molecules in a liquid stay close together, but move about. The molecules in a gas move about very rapidly and rebound from one another. Answers: solid – butter, wood, salt, ice lolly (before it melts), candle, paper, nail; liquid – honey, ketchup; gas – bubbles, inside a balloon, steam.	QCA Unit 4D 'Solids, liquids and how they can be separated'. Builds on Unit 2D 'Grouping and changing materials', Unit 3C 'Characteristics of materials' and Unit 3D 'Rocks and soils'. NC Sc3 (3) Separating mixtures of materials.	ES Earth and space: Changing materials – Level C/D	AT3 Level 3/4
page 58	Physical and chemical changes	To understand the difference between physical and chemical changes.	It will be useful to discuss the concept of physical changes with the three states of water and to have in the classroom a glass of water, an ice cube and a boiling kettle [careful supervision is needed]. In a physical change no new substance is formed or destroyed, there is no change in weight, it can usually be reversed and the energy changes are usually small. In chemical changes the substance is changed and new substances are formed, there is a change in weight, a reverse change is difficult and the energy changes are often large. Answers: the ice lolly, wood, drink can and heated milk undergo a physical change, while the yoghurt and bread are the result of chemical changes.	QCA Unit 4D 'Solids, liquids and how they can be separated'. Builds on Unit 2D 'Grouping and changing materials', Unit 3C 'Characteristics of materials' and Unit 3D 'Rocks and soils'. NC Sc3 (3) Separating mixtures of materials.	ES Earth and space: Changing materials – Level C/D	AT3 Level 3/4
page 59	Feeling forces	To begin understanding that forces can be measured and compared. To recognise that the pull of gravity gives us a sense of 'up' and 'down', and that it also gives a measure of weight.	Careful pairing of children who can work accurately and carefully together will be needed to complete this activity. They should find that the larger the object, the bigger its downward force and the harder it pulls the hand down.	QCA Unit 4E 'Friction'. Builds on Unit 3E 'Magnets and springs'. NC Sc4 (2) Forces and motion.	ES Energy and forces: Forces and their effects – Level C	AT4 Level 3
page 60	Friction – friend or foe?	To recognise friction as an important force and to begin to understand friction in everyday contexts.	A discussion on what friction is together with a simple example, such as a shoe on wet tiles or rough carpet, would be a useful starting point. Sometimes friction can be useful, for example, when it prevents us from sliding down a slope. Friction can also be a nuisance, when we have to pedal harder due to a poorly-oiled bicycle. In some situations, friction may be helpful and unhelpful, for example, when sliding down a rope friction hurts your hand, but it also enables you to hold onto the rope and not to slide too quickly.	QCA Unit 4E 'Friction'. Builds on Unit 3E 'Magnets and springs'. NC Sc4 (2) Forces and motion.	ES Energy and forces: Forces and their effects – Level C	AT4 Level 3
page 61	The effect of rubber on friction?	To measure forces using standard measures. To observe that rubber on a surface increases the amount of friction that that surface can exert.	The children will need to be familiar with how to use a force meter for this activity. The piece of wood is always more difficult to move when the elastic bands are in place. This is because the elastic bands increase the friction between the piece of wood and the table. Follow this up with a discussion on why tyres and rubber-soled footwear have tread patterns.	QCA Unit 4E 'Friction'. Builds on Unit 3E 'Magnets and springs'. NC Sc4 (2) Forces and motion.	ES Energy and forces: Forces and their effects – Level C/D	AT4 Level 3/4
page 62	Parachute design	To begin to develop fair tests and understand the force of air resistance.	This is a much easier activity if each child [or pair] is provided with two copies of the photocopiable sheet. The children could also compare the effectiveness of circular and square parachutes to consider the best shape for a parachute design.	QCA Unit 4E 'Friction'. Builds on Unit 3E 'Magnets and springs'. NC Sc4 (2) Forces and motion.	ES Energy and forces: Forces and their effects – Level D	AT4 Level 3/4
page 63	The best size	To continue using a fair test, looking for patterns in results and interpreting and suggesting explanations.	Each parachute should be cut out of each square so that the circle is the biggest size possible and just touches the edge of the square of paper. Ensure that each drop is carried out from the same height with the same lump of Plasticine for a fair test. The 'best' result will be the slowest, but if the parachute is dropped too low it will not open. There is a link between the size of the parachute and the height from which it is dropped.	QCA Unit 4E 'Friction'. Builds on Unit 3E 'Magnets and springs'. NC Sc4 (2) Forces and motion.	ES Energy and forces: Forces and their effects – Level D	AT4 Level 3/4

Page	Activity	Objective	Teachers' notes	QCA Scheme of Work and National Curriculum links	Scottish Curriculum links	KS2 Levels
page 64	What can electricity do?	To understand the different ways in which electricity is used in the home.	It will be useful to find examples of the different uses of electricity – heat, light, movement, sound, magnetic – before the activity. Try to think of ones that are not on the photocopiable sheet. The sheet is written so that the children will think of electricity as a form of energy which changes into another form. Some answers involve more than one change; for example, television – sound, light and magnetism.	QCA Unit 4F 'Circuits and conductors'. Builds on Unit 2F 'Using electricity'. NC Sc4 (1) Electricity.	ES Energy and forces: Properties and uses of energy – Level C	AT4 Level 3
page 65	Making it flow	To understand that there are conductors and insulators of electricity.	You will need at least 12 materials that are a mixture of those that conduct and those that insulate (poor conductors). The children should know how to connect an electrical circuit. They will find that more metals conduct electricity if their surfaces are clean. A short length of pencil lead, however, will also conduct a current and the children may need help to understand that this is not a metal.	QCA Unit 4F 'Circuits and conductors'. Builds on Unit 2F 'Using electricity'. NC Sc4 (1) Electricity.	ES Energy and forces: Properties and uses of energy – Level C	AT4 Level 3
page 66	Making switches	To understand that a device will not work unless there is a complete circuit and that switches are used to make many appliances work.	It is important to check that all the batteries and bulbs work before starting this activity.	QCA Unit 4F 'Circuits and conductors'. Builds on Unit 2F 'Using electricity'. NC Sc4 (1) Electricity.	ES Energy and forces: Properties and uses of energy – Level C	AT4 Level 3
page 67	A question and answer machine	To construct a more complicated circuit and develop the concept of complete circuits and switches.	This can be developed over a period of several lessons and the completed 'machines' should be left in the classroom for everyone to try. The questions and answers could be designed to fit a variety of classroom topics.	QCA Unit 4F 'Circuits and conductors'. Builds on Unit 2F 'Using electricity'. NC Sc4 (1) Electricity.	ES Energy and forces: Properties and uses of energy – Level C	AT4 Level 3/4
page 68	The respiratory system	To understand how a healthy respiratory system works.	This is a difficult activity and it will be important to read through the sheet with the children discussing the vocabulary and how the lungs work. The children will see that air escapes from the straw as the diaphragm is pushed in and the balloon collapses.	QCA Unit 5A 'Keeping healthy'. Builds on Unit 3A 'Teeth and eating' and Unit 4A 'Moving and growing'. NC Sc2 (1) Life processes; (2) Humans and other animals.	ES Living things and the processes of life: The processes of life – Level D	AT2 Level 3/4
page 69	The heart	To begin learning about how the heart works. To investigate how a valve works.	This is a difficult activity and it is important to read through the sheet with the children discussing the vocabulary and how the heart works. Answers: left-hand side names – aorta, right auricle, valve, right ventricle; right-hand side names – left auricle, left ventricle. Safety note: Ensure the children use the craft knife correctly.	QCA Unit 5A 'Keeping healthy'. Builds on Unit 3A 'Teeth and eating' and Unit 4A 'Moving and growing'. NC Sc2 (1) Life processes; (2) Humans and other animals.	ES Living things and the processes of life: The processes of life – Level C	AT2 Level 3/4
page 70	Heartbeat rate	To understand how heartbeat (pulse rate) is affected by exercise.	The vocabulary is quite difficult and may need explaining. Each child needs to be able to find their pulse quickly so it is important to check that they can do this before the activity. The heartbeat increases as the exercises become more strenuous because the muscles and organs use up more oxygen and food. Safety note: Ensure that none of the children suffer from illnesses which prevent them from participating in strenuous exercise.	QCA Unit 5A 'Keeping healthy'. Builds on Unit 3A 'Teeth and eating' and Unit 4A 'Moving and growing'. NC Sc2 (1) Life processes; (2) Humans and other animals.	ES Living things and the processes of life: The processes of life – Level C	AT2 Level 3/4
page 71	A balanced diet	To understand how a balanced diet is important for health.	It will be useful to discuss some examples of what a balanced diet actually means before the children complete this activity.	QCA Unit 5A 'Keeping healthy'. Builds on Unit 3A 'Teeth and eating' and Unit 4A 'Moving and growing'. NC Sc2 (1) Life processes; (2) Humans and other animals.	ES Living things and the processes of life: The processes of life – Level D	AT2 Level 3/4
page 72	Hygiene	To understand that hygiene and keeping clean is all important for good health.	After the children complete the activity there should be a full discussion about washing before and after certain activities and how important it is for our health. We should wash our hands before eating and preparing food. We should wash our hands after: patting an animal, changing a baby's nappy, cleaning out a hamster cage, and using and cleaning the toilet. Hands should be washed before and after looking after a sick person.	QCA Unit 5A 'Keeping healthy'. Builds on Unit 3A 'Teeth and eating' and Unit 4A 'Moving and growing'. NC Sc2 (1) Life processes; (2) Humans and other animals.	ES Living things and the processes of life: The processes of life – Level D	AT2 Level 3/4
page 73	The life-cycle of a flowering plant	To understand that there are distinct processes and stages in every life-cycle.	It is important that this activity is part of a series of lessons that look at plants at different stages in their growth. Relate this activity to the life-cycle of local trees and seasonal changes.	QCA Unit 5B 'Life cycles'. Builds on Unit 2A 'Health and growth' and Unit 3B 'Helping plants grow well'. NC Sc2 (1) Life processes; (4) Variation and classification; (5) Living things in their environment.	ES Living things and the processes of life: Variety and characteristic features; The processes of life – Level D	AT2 Level 4
page 74	Animal life-cycles	To understand that there are distinct processes and stages in every life-cycle. To introduce the concept of metamorphosis.	It is essential to consider the differences in animal life-cycles especially between mammals, reptiles, insects, and so on. Answers: things which are the same in both types of life-cycles – mating takes place before young are born, the female produces eggs, the young grow into adults; things which are different – the young do not always look like the parents, some animals undergo changes in shape and form before becoming an adult, cats give birth to live young whereas insects lay eggs.	QCA Unit 5B 'Life cycles'. Builds on Unit 2A 'Health and growth' and Unit 3B 'Helping plants grow well'. NC Sc2 (1) Life processes; (4) Variation and classification; (5) Living things in their environment.	ES Living things and the processes of life: Variety and characteristic features; The processes of life – Level D	AT2 Level 4
page 75	How much light do plants need?	To understand the role of light in plant growth.	The seedlings with the greatest amount of sunlight should grow best. Plants grow towards sunlight (phototropism) so the seedlings will bend towards the light source. This could be part of a series of experiments and observations on plant growth. Consider what else a plant needs for healthy growth, such as water and heat.	QCA Unit 5B 'Life cycles'. Builds on Unit 2A 'Health and growth' and Unit 3B 'Helping plants grow well'. NC Sc2 (1) Life processes; (4) Variation and classification; (5) Living things in their environment.	ES Living things and the processes of life: Variety and characteristic features; The processes of life – Level C/D	AT2 Level 3/4
page 76	The parts of a flower	To be familiar with the structure of plants and the names of parts of a flower.	In some common flowers it is difficult to recognise the parts – but it is important to have several different types. Daffodils are excellent to take to pieces as all their parts are very easily seen. Explain that the flower allows the plant to reproduce and both male (stamen) and female (carpel) parts are usually present.	QCA Unit 5B 'Life cycles'. Builds on Unit 2A 'Health and growth' and Unit 3B 'Helping plants grow well'. NC Sc2 (1) Life processes; (4) Variation and classification; (5) Living things in their environment.	ES Living things and the processes of life: Variety and characteristic features; The processes of life – Level D	AT2 Level 4
page 77	Pollination	To begin to understand the process of pollination and how reproduction is important to the survival of the species.	All children should use a microscope because some of the pollens are spectacular. It will be useful to refer back to the previous activity and the development of the seeds [ovary] in common flowers. The insects may be found on one colour of flower but the presence of scent which signals that food in the form of nectar is available is the main attraction for insects. This sheet can be given as homework so that children can investigate gardens at home, if appropriate.	QCA Unit 5B 'Life cycles'. Builds on Unit 2A 'Health and growth' and Unit 3B 'Helping plants grow well'. NC Sc2 (1) Life processes; (4) Variation and classification; (5) Living things in their environment.	ES Living things and the processes of life: Variety and characteristic features; The processes of life – Level D	AT2 Level 3/4

NO FUSS

SCHOLASTIC
www.scholastic.co.uk

Page	Activity	Objective	Teachers' notes	QCA Scheme of Work and National Curriculum links	Scottish Curriculum links	KS2 Levels
page 78	Reproduction and the human life-cycle	To learn that animals reproduce as part of their life-cycle. To introduce names of the female and male reproductive organs.	This activity can be used as part of a programme for Personal, social and health education. Male reproductive organs: A – sperm duct; B – testis; C – penis; D – scrotum. Female reproductive organs: E – oviduct; F – ovary; G – uterus; H – vagina.	QCA Unit 5B 'Life cycles'. Builds on Unit 2A 'Health and growth' and Unit 3B 'Helping plants grow well'. NC Sc2 (I) Life processes; (4) Variation and classification; (5) Living things in their environment.	ES Living things and the processes of life: Variety and characteristic features; The processes of life – Level D	AT2 Level 3/4
page 79	Looking at gases	To look at where gases are found and to recognise that air is a gas.	It will be useful to remind the children of the force air exerts by referring to the parachute activities. Gases are difficult to observe, but their presence can often be detected by looking for clues; for example, the effect of air resistance on parachutes. Answers: the bubbles of air pumped through the water in the fish tank provide oxygen for the fish; tanks supply the diver with oxygen while he is underwater; washing on the line is moved by the air (wind) as it is dried; hot air causes the balloon to rise.	QCA Unit 5C 'Gases around us'. Builds on Unit 3D 'Rocks and soils', Unit 4D 'Solids, liquids and how they can be separated' and Unit 4E 'Friction'. NC Sc3 (I) Grouping and classifying materials.	ES Earth and space: Materials from Earth – Level D	AT3 Level 3/4
page 80	Making and collecting gases	To begin to understand that gases flow and are able to fill spaces. To observe that gases can be made by mixing materials.	It might be necessary to test the amounts of material required which will vary according to the size of the bottle. The reaction between bicarbonate of soda and vinegar is immediate; the children see, feel and hear the gas (carbon dioxide) as it escapes from the bottle into the atmosphere. The balloon will expand as the gas is collected. It is important to discuss the findings from this activity to extend the children's vocabulary. Safety note: Only plastic bottles should be used when mixing substances that react together.	QCA Unit 5C 'Gases around us'. Builds on Unit 3D 'Rocks and soils', Unit 4D 'Solids, liquids and how they can be separated' and Unit 4E 'Friction'. NC Sc3 (I) Grouping and classifying materials.	ES Earth and space: Materials from Earth – Level D	AT3 Level 3/4
page 81	Comparing solids, liquids and gases	To understand that gases can be distinguished from solids and liquids by their properties, but there are also some similarities.	A discussion about solids, liquids and gases and their properties would be useful before doing this activity. A solid keeps its own shape, can sometimes be used for building and is usually easy to handle. A liquid flows downhill, flows easily through a pipe, drips, has no definite shape and takes the shape of the container it is in. A gas flows easily through a pipe, spreads out in all directions, has no definite shape and can be squashed into a smaller volume. Containers: solids – schoolbag, jar, cupboard, box; liquids – jar, bottle, hose-pipe, straw, flask; gases – oxygen cylinder, balloon, pair of lungs.	QCA Unit 5C 'Gases around us'. Builds on Unit 3D 'Rocks and soils', Unit 4D 'Solids, liquids and how they can be separated' and Unit 4E 'Friction'. NC Sc3 (I) Grouping and classifying materials.	ES Earth and space: Materials from Earth – Level D	AT3 Level 4
page 82	How is the 'greenhouse effect' produced?	To relate observations and conclusions to scientific knowledge and understanding.	The 'greenhouse effect' (global warming) is caused by a layer of polluting gases collecting high up in the atmosphere. These gases act like the glass in a greenhouse, preventing heat from escaping easily and so causing the surface of the Earth to warm up. The children should observe that the soil in the container under the glass is likely to have a higher temperature than that in the other container.	QCA Unit 5C 'Gases around us'. Builds on Unit 3D 'Rocks and soils', Unit 4D 'Solids, liquids and how they can be separated' and Unit 4E 'Friction'. NC Sc3 (I) Grouping and classifying materials.	ES Earth and space: Materials from Earth – Level D	AT3 Level 3/4
page 83	The water cycle	To explain the water cycle in terms of water changing states. To consider how water is used by humans.	It will be important to learn and understand the vocabulary of the water cycle. Answers: I evaporation; 2 water vapour; 3 condensation; 4 precipitation; 5 runoff; 6 groundwater; 7 irrigation; 8 purification; 9 evaporation.	QCA Unit 5D 'Changing state'. Builds on Unit 4D 'Solids, liquids and how they can be separated' and Unit 5C 'Gases around us'. NC Sc3 (2) Changing materials.	ES Earth and space: Materials from Earth; Changing materials – Level D	AT3 Level 3/4
page 84	Using water at school	To be aware of how much water is used (and wasted) at school. To make observations and measurements.	This is a long and detailed activity that can be completed over several days. It should raise the children's awareness of how water is used at school and they could devise and initiate measures to reduce the waste. In order to work out how much water is used, allow the average number of times that the toilets are flushed and hand basins are filled to be three times each per person per day. The amount of water used in the classroom sinks could be calculated on the basis of one classroom and then multiplied by the number of classes. To find out how much water is used in the kitchens, ask the school cook to keep a tally and encourage the children to interview the cook to access this information.	QCA Unit 5D 'Changing state'. Builds on Unit 4D 'Solids, liquids and how they can be separated' and Unit 5C 'Gases around us'. NC Sc3 (2) Changing materials.	ES Earth and space: Materials from Earth; Changing materials – Level D	AT3 Level 3/4
page 85	How much water do you use?	To be aware of how much water is used (and wasted) at home. To make observations and measurements.	This activity is a homework project over a period of a week and the children must be able to tally. Use the results to produce a graph. Devise water-saving measures for the home.	QCA Unit 5D 'Changing state'. Builds on Unit 4D 'Solids, liquids and how they can be separated' and Unit 5C 'Gases around us'. NC Sc3 (2) Changing materials.	ES Earth and space: Earth; Changing materials – Level D	AT3 Level 3/4
page 86	Why is it hotter in summer than in winter?	To understand that the Earth's axis is tilted and it is this tilt which produces the higher temperatures of summer.	You will need a dark room for this activity and the children will need to work together sensibly. When the North Pole is tilted away from the lamp (winter), the light is most intense at the Equator and very diffused in the northern hemisphere. When the North Pole is tilted towards the Sun (summer), the light is more intense in the northern hemisphere resulting in warmer weather.	QCA Unit 5E 'Earth, Sun and Moon'. Builds on Unit ID 'Light and dark' and Unit 3F 'Light and shadows'. NC Sc4 (4) The Earth and beyond.	ES Earth and space: Earth in space – Level D	AT4 Level 4
page 87	Seasonal changes	To understand that the Earth rotates around the Sun, which has an effect on the seasons of the year. To understand that animals and plants are affected by seasons.	This activity is worth discussing in detail before it is completed because some children may live in places where seasonal changes are not obvious.	QCA Unit 5E 'Earth, Sun and Moon'. Builds on Unit ID 'Light and dark' and Unit 3F 'Light and shadows'. NC Sc4 (4) The Earth and beyond.	ES Earth and space: Earth in space – Level D	AT4 Level 4
page 88	Build a sundial	To know that the apparent position of the Sun changes over the course of a day and that this movement can be measured in time.	This activity needs a whole sunny day to make it work. Once the clock is constructed it could be tested on another sunny day. Safety note: NEVER look directly at the Sun.	QCA Unit 5E 'Earth, Sun and Moon'. Builds on Unit ID 'Light and dark' and Unit 3F 'Light and shadows'. NC Sc4 (4) The Earth and beyond.	ES Earth and space: Earth in space – Level D	AT4 Level 3/4
page 89	Earth and Moon dance	To understand the relationship between the Earth rotating on its axis, the Moon rotating around the Earth and the Earth rotating around the Sun.	This is a practical way to help understand a complicated process. It is best completed in a large space such as the school hall. The children could act out simple Solar Systems in groups of three, each child being the Sun, the Moon or the Earth.	QCA Unit 5E 'Earth, Sun and Moon'. Builds on Unit ID 'Light and dark' and Unit 3F 'Light and shadows'. NC Sc4 (4) The Earth and beyond.	ES Earth and space: Earth in space – Level D	AT4 Level 4

Page	Activity	Objective	Teachers' notes	QCA Scheme of Work and National Curriculum links	Scottish Curriculum links	KS2 Levels
page 90	Changes in the moon	To understand that the positions of the Moon, Earth and Sun affect how we see the Moon's shape.	This is a complicated activity but it is important to complete it. If there are clear nights it will help the children understand the different shapes of the Moon's appearance. Use photocopiable page 89 'Earth and Moon dance' to remind the children of the direction in which the Moon moves around the Earth, and that the Moon also spins on its own axis.	QCA Unit 5E 'Earth, Sun and Moon'. Builds on Unit 1D 'Light and dark' and Unit 3F 'Light and shadows'. NC Sc4 (4) The Earth and beyond.	ES Earth and space: Earth in space – Level D	AT4 Level 4
page 91	Solids and shadows	To understand that shadows are formed when light is blocked.	You will need a darkened room for this activity and a good collection of 3-D shapes. The children should observe that a single source of light illuminates only part of an object, leaving the rest in shadow.	QCA Unit 5E 'Earth, Sun and Moon'. Builds on Unit 1D 'Light and dark' and Unit 3F 'Light and shadows'. NC Sc4 (4) The Earth and beyond.	ES Earth and space: Earth in space – Level D	AT4 Level 3/4
page 92	The senses: hearing	To begin to understand that vibrations from sound sources travel through the air to the ear. To investigate how far away we can hear sound and if two ears are better than one.	Hearing impaired children will need particular support with this activity. Encourage the children to invent games to test their ability to discriminate between sounds.	QCA Unit 5F 'Changing sounds'. Builds on Unit 1F 'Sound and hearing'. NC Sc4 (3) Light and sound.	ES Energy and forces: Properties and uses of energy – Level D	AT4 Level 3/4
page 93	Sound survey	To make careful observations about sound and to draw conclusions.	Hearing impaired children will need particular support with this activity. Children (and adults) are always surprised by the number of sounds around us which we take for granted.	QCA Unit 5F 'Changing sounds'. Builds on Unit 1F 'Sound and hearing'. NC Sc4 (3) Light and sound.	ES Energy and forces: Properties and uses of energy – Level D	AT4 Level 3/4
page 94	What makes sounds?	To understand that sounds are made when objects or materials vibrate.	Hearing impaired children will need particular support with this activity. It would be helpful to discuss the term 'vibration'. This sheet will help the children understand what vibration is by looking, feeling and listening carefully. Encourage them to record what they can see and feel when sounds are made.	QCA Unit 5F 'Changing sounds'. Builds on Unit 1F 'Sound and hearing'. NC Sc4 (3) Light and sound.	ES Energy and forces: Properties and uses of energy – Level D	AT4 Level 3/4
page 95	High and low sounds	To recognise that the term 'pitch' refers to how high or low a sound is.	Hearing impaired children will need particular support with this activity. It will be useful to continue this activity by listening to the variety of sounds made by musical instruments. The children should begin to understand that we get higher pitched sounds when smaller things vibrate. For instance, the shorter the length of elastic band or smaller the amount of air in the bottle, the higher the pitch of the note produced.	QCA Unit 5F 'Changing sounds'. Builds on Unit 1F 'Sound and hearing'. NC Sc4 (3) Light and sound.	ES Energy and forces: Properties and uses of energy – Level D	AT4 Level 3/4
page 96	How earthworms move	To collect and record evidence in an appropriate manner.	Collect earthworms by sprinkling water on a lawn. Pupils must not handle the earthworms with a cut finger. An earthworm has backwards-pointing bristles on its underside for gripping, which can be felt when the finger is rubbed from tail to head. The bristles make a scratching sound on the towel. Assess the children for their use of simple apparatus to make careful observations. Emphasise to the children that the earthworm needs to be returned to its natural habitat after the experiment.	QCA Unit 5/6H 'Enquiry in environmental and technological contexts'. Relates to Unit 6A 'Interdependence and adaptation'. NC Sc2 (5) Living things in their environment.	ES Living things and the processes of life: Interaction of living things with their environment – Level D	AT2 Level 3/4
page 97	Investigating birds' beaks	Evaluate the evidence collected and consider its limitations.	Begin by discussing bird tables or feeding ducks. Collect tweezers (pigeon), chopsticks (sparrow), sugar tongs (crow), and salad servers (duck). Let the children extract the seeds and biscuits for bags of 'wild bird seed' and put it into dishes from where they can be pecked out in a given time by a model beak. The implements for the model beaks can be improvised in other ways by using other pieces of equipment.	QCA Unit 5/6H 'Enquiry in environmental and technological contexts'. Relates to Unit 6A 'Interdependence and adaptation'. NC Sc2 (5) Living things in their environment.	ES Living things and the processes of life: Interaction of living things with their environment – Level D	AT2 Level 3/4
page 98	Seed dispersal	To make careful observations. To understand how plants colonise their local habitats by being dependent on certain characteristics.	This activity will be more successful if it is completed in the autumn when there are lots of different seeds available. The four main methods of seed dispersal are: wind, animal, explosion, and water. Possible answers: wind – the dandelion has a parachute effect helping the seed to float in the air; animal – the blackberry is small, round and easy to swallow, the burdock has lots of spiny parts which catch in the fur of an animal; explosion – the lupin has a long seed pod and the seeds are well spaced out so that when the pod opens the seeds are spread over a wide area; water – the coconut is completely sealed and waterproof so that water will not get inside and sink it. The seeds are dispersed in the following way: explosion – broom; animal – elderberry and agrimony; wind – sycamore and ash; water – water lily.	QCA Unit 6A 'Interdependence and adaptation'. Builds on Unit 3B 'Helping plants grow well' and Unit 4B 'Habitats'. NC Sc2 (1) Life processes; (5) Living things in their environment.	ES Living things and the processes of life: The processes of life – Level D	AT2 Level 4
page 99	Food chains	To understand that food chains represent feeding relationships.	There needs to be an initial discussion to help understand 'producers' and 'consumers'. Possible food chains are: shrub → slug → hedgehog; wheat → vole → tawny owl; grass → roe deer → human; grass → rabbit → human; wheat → vole → fox.	QCA Unit 6A 'Interdependence and adaptation'. Builds on Unit 3B 'Helping plants grow well' and Unit 4B 'Habitats'. NC Sc2 (1) Life processes; (5) Living things in their environment.	ES Living things and the processes of life: The processes of life – Level D	AT2 Level 4
page 100	Plant adaptations	To understand how different plants are suited to their environment.	It will be useful to read through the descriptions of each plant on the sheet and discuss any relevant issues first. The cactus is adapted to desert life in the following ways: the roots spread a long way and are close to the soil surface to obtain as much water as possible, the stem is large to store water, the plane is shaped so that water runs off it into the roots, the shiny surface of the plant reflects light and the leaves are reduced to spines to reduce water loss so the plant does not overheat. The water lily is adapted to life in water in the following ways: the leaves are flat so that a large surface area faces the sun, the waxy surface of the leaves prevent them from becoming waterlogged and sinking, it produces seeds which can float, and the long stem has roots which grow into the mud to anchor it.	QCA Unit 6A 'Interdependence and adaptation'. Builds on Unit 3B 'Helping plants grow well' and Unit 4B 'Habitats'. NC Sc2 (1) Life processes; (5) Living things in their environment.	ES Living things and the processes of life: The processes of life – Level D	AT2 Level 4
page 101	Roots	To understand that water and nutrients are taken through the roots.	This activity needs preparation and there needs to be a supply of growing plants in pots. A plant has roots to anchor it into the ground and to help in the uptake of water and nutrients. The water in the jar will be soaked up by the cotton cloth and will be transferred to the saucer by capillary action. This is similar to the way a root soaks up water. Roots will grow from the spider plantlet's base.	QCA Unit 6A 'Interdependence and adaptation'. Builds on Unit 3B 'Helping plants grow well' and Unit 4B 'Habitats'. NC Sc2 (1) Life processes; (5) Living things in their environment.	ES Living things and the processes of life: The processes of life – Level D	AT2 Level 3/4

SCHOLASTIC
www.scholastic.co.uk

Page	Activity	Objective	Teachers' notes	QCA Scheme of Work and National Curriculum links	Scottish Curriculum links	KS2 Levels
page 102	Using the Earth's materials	To understand that natural resources are diminishing and with time some materials will be harder to find.	The concept of recycling and its importance needs to be discussed before completing this activity. With careful management, the recycling and production of some materials may be sufficient for our needs. Oil and metal ores are limited in their supply. Hardwood trees (for wood and rubber) are disappearing faster than they can grow. Softwood trees grow more quickly and could give a sustainable supply. The use of hardwoods should be avoided (red); plastic, metal, natural fabrics, and paper should be used carefully (amber); softwood and glass should be used widely (green).	QCA Unit 6A 'Interdependence and adaptation'. Builds on Unit 3B 'Helping plants grow well' and Unit 4B 'Habitats'. NC Sc2 (1) Life processes; (5) Living things in their environment.	ES Living things and the processes of life: The processes of life – Level D	AT2 Level 3/4
page 103	Renewable and non-renewable resources	To recognise the kinds of materials that cannot be replaced and to use scientific ideas to explain current problems	The concept of renewable resources needs to be discussed before completing this activity. Some resources are classed as non-renewable because they took so long to re-form; for example, fossil fuels such as coal and oil. Extend this activity by looking at how some renewable resources are used.	QCA Unit 6A 'Interdependence and adaptation'. Builds on Unit 3B 'Helping plants grow well' and Unit 4B 'Habitats'. NC Sc2 (1) Life processes; (5) Living things in their environment.	ES Living things and the processes of life: The processes of life – Level D	AT2 Level 4
page 104	Will it rot?	To recognise that micro-organisms can cause food to decay.	Following this experiment, it would be useful to discuss safe food handling and hygiene. Safety note: Any relevant health and safety issues need to be followed when completing this activity. Do not open the bags once they are prepared as spurs from moulds are harmful.	QCA Unit 6B 'Micro-organisms'. Builds on Unit 3A 'Teeth and eating' and Unit 6A 'Interdependence and adaptation'. NC Sc2 (5) Living things in their environment.	ES Living things and the processes of life: Variety and characteristic features – Level D	AT2 Level 4
page 105	Making compost	To begin to explain some causes of decay. To investigate the use of compost.	This is a long-term activity and could be part of a wider environmental project. Decay occurs due to decomposers such as bacteria, fungi and earthworms. The processes involved produce heat and the compost can steam. The smell produced by rotting food is caused by the nitrogen and sulphur compounds that are formed. The children should find that the seed planted in compost will do better than the other.	QCA Unit 6B 'Micro-organisms'. Builds on Unit 3A 'Teeth and eating' and Unit 6A 'Interdependence and adaptation'. NC Sc2 (5) Living things in their environment.	ES Living things and the processes of life: Variety and characteristic features – Level D	AT2 Level 3/4
page 106	Micro-organisms	To recognise that micro-organisms can cause illness or decay, but preventative measures can be taken when handling and storing food.	Washing hands gets rid of many bacteria which could cause food to become contaminated; low temperatures do not destroy bacteria but prevent them from multiplying further; high cooking temperatures destroy bacteria, making food safe to eat if eaten immediately; the cooking and washing processes involved in canning and bottling remove bacteria and the sealed containers eliminate the air which can carry bacteria. Bacteria needs these conditions to grow: moisture, oxygen, warm temperature, lack of direct sunlight. It might be useful to ask children if they can think of other ways to prevent or reduce bacteria in foods, for example, freezing, sell-by dates, and so on.	QCA Unit 6B 'Micro-organisms'. Builds on Unit 3A 'Teeth and eating' and Unit 6A 'Interdependence and adaptation'. NC Sc2 (5) Living things in their environment.	ES Living things and the processes of life: Variety and characteristic features – Level D	AT2 Level 3/4
page 107	Food care and storage	To recognise that micro-organisms can cause illness or decay, but preventative measures can be taken when handling and storing food.	You will need lots of packets and tin labels. This activity examines the many ways of preserving different foods by adding substances that extend the life of the food. Fresh food contains the most nourishment because food preservation methods destroy some nutrients. Additives are natural or synthetic chemicals which are used to prevent food from going bad for a long time, make food look appetising and make it tasty. But are they good for us?	QCA Unit 6B 'Micro-organisms'. Builds on Unit 3A 'Teeth and eating' and Unit 6A 'Interdependence and adaptation'. NC Sc2 (5) Living things in their environment.	ES Living things and the processes of life: Variety and characteristic features – Level D	
page 108	Microbes and disease	To use scientific ideas to explain some causes of illness.	Giving children the opportunity to explain how they feel when they are ill would be a useful starting point. Talk about how the body fights back and glands swelling up in the throat are part of this process.	QCA Unit 6B 'Micro-organisms'. Builds on Unit 3A 'Teeth and eating' and Unit 6A 'Interdependence and adaptation'. NC Sc2 (5) Living things in their environment.	ES Living things and the processes of life: Variety and characteristic features – Level D	AT2 Level 4
page 109	Separating substances	To begin to understand the concept of filtering and evaporation.	The children will need help with the vocabulary such as filtering, suspension, solution and so on. Filtration involves the use of a barrier to hold back particles of solids. Groundwater is filtered as it passes through layers of rock and soil. The solution passing through the filter is called the filtrate; insoluble material on the filter is the residue. The children will see that the muddy water becomes clearer as it filters through.	QCA Unit 6C 'More about dissolving'. Builds on Unit 4D 'Solids, liquids and how they can be separated' and Unit 5C 'Gases around us'. NC Sc3 (2) Changing materials; (3) Separating mixtures of materials.	ES Earth and space: Changing materials – Level D	AT3 Level 4/5
page 110	Chromatography	To observe how one colour can be made up of different colours.	Some colours will spread out more quickly than others. A discussion of mixing paint colours would be a useful comparison to look at the ways in which mixing colours can make new ones.	QCA Unit 6C 'More about dissolving'. Builds on Unit 4D 'Solids, liquids and how they can be separated' and Unit 5C 'Gases around us'. NC Sc3 (2) Changing materials; (3) Separating mixtures of materials.	ES Earth and space: Changing materials – Level D	AT3 Level 4
page 111	Soil drainage	To evaluate observations related to suspensions and filtering.	It is important to discuss the children's answers to the final four questions and to share ideas. Water drains through sandy soils faster than through clay soils, which retain more water. Therefore, it would be easier to walk over sandy soil after heavy rain. In theory plants would grow better in a clay soil in dry weather; but in reality the clay soils tend to crack when dry, exposing the plant roots to the air.	QCA Unit 6C 'More about dissolving'. Builds on Unit 4D 'Solids, liquids and how they can be separated' and Unit 5C 'Gases around us'. NC Sc3 (2) Changing materials; (3) Separating mixtures of materials.	ES Earth and space: Changing materials – Level D	AT3 Level 4
page 112	Making chemical changes	To begin to understand that some changes cannot be reversed and can produce new substances.	Steel is mostly iron. Iron combines with oxygen in the air to form iron oxide (rust). Water helps to speed up the chemical action. As wood burns, water, carbon dioxide, methane, pentane, hexane and octane are produced. There are safety issues related to burning substances so some of this activity may be best completed as a class demonstration.	QCA Unit 6D 'Reversible and irreversible changes'. Builds on Unit 2D 'Grouping and changing materials', Unit 5D 'Changing state' and Unit 6C 'More about dissolving'. NC Sc3 (1) Grouping and classifying materials.	ES Earth and space: Changing materials – Level D	AT3 Level 4/5
page 113	Manufactured changes	To classify some changes as irreversible. To differentiate between raw and manufactured materials.	There are many more examples of raw and manufactured materials and it would be useful to extend the sheet through discussion of raw materials and manufactured changes based on objects and material in the classroom and in the school. Answers: glass, steel, plastic, flour, aluminium and petrol are manufactured; the rest are raw materials.	QCA Unit 6D 'Reversible and irreversible changes'. Builds on Unit 2D 'Grouping and changing materials', Unit 5D 'Changing state' and Unit 6C 'More about dissolving'. NC Sc3 (1) Grouping and classifying materials.	ES Earth and space: Changing materials – Level D	AT3 Level 4/5

Page	Activity	Objective	Teachers' notes	QCA Scheme of Work and National Curriculum links	Scottish Curriculum links	KS2 Levels
page 114	Changes in strength	To consider how to make paper stronger. To suggest explanations for observations made.	It will be important to discuss the children's findings because there may be a margin of error in the results. Paper which is folded or rolled will be much stronger than flat paper. Extend this activity by making a bridge from newspaper that will stand. Either have a competition to make the longest bridge or strongest bridge (over a standard distance) from a limited length of paper.	QCA Unit 6D 'Reversible and irreversible changes'. Builds on Unit 2D 'Grouping and changing materials', Unit 5D 'Changing state' and Unit 6C 'More about dissolving'. NC Sc3 (1) Grouping and classifying materials.	ES Earth and space: Changing materials – Level A	AT3 Level 4
page 115	Forces at work	To begin to understand that forces can be measured and compared. To know that pushing, pulling and twisting are all forces.	Children need to be encouraged to discuss this activity and to work accurately. The wheelbarrow, ball and bulldozer are moved by pushing; the dog is pulling its owner; the jar lid is removed by twisting; the door is opened by twisting the knob and then is either pushed or pulled. The biggest force is the bulldozer.	QCA Unit 6E 'Forces in action'. Builds on Unit 4E 'Friction'. NC Sc4 (2) Forces and motion.	ES Energy and forces: Forces and their effects – Level C	AT4 Level 3/4
page 116	Measuring forces	To measure and compare common forces.	The stretch in the elastic band is measured against an arbitrary scale and indicates the size of the force. This activity can be followed up with a lesson on using a Newton meter [force meter].	QCA Unit 6E 'Forces in action'. Builds on Unit 4E 'Friction'. NC Sc4 (2) Forces and motion.	ES Energy and forces: Forces and their effects – Level D	AT4 Level 4/5
page 117	Force meters	To develop skills in making and repeating measurements	There needs to be a variety of small objects in the classroom for the children to use for this activity. A Newton meter will be required for this activity. Answers: 5N, 4.5N, 3.2N, 0.5N, 2IN, 0.6N, 11N, 0.3N, 0.7N, 7N.	QCA Unit 6E 'Forces in action'. Builds on Unit 4E 'Friction'. NC Sc4 (2) Forces and motion.	ES Energy and forces: Forces and their effects – Level D	AT4 Level 4/5
page 118	Investigating gravity	To understand that as objects fall to Earth, the speed accelerates. To develop skills in making measurements and using results to draw conclusions.	Check whether the children remember how to measure in metres and centimetres. The children should begin to understand that objects that fall greater distances have time to reach a greater speed, therefore increasing the impact on landing. They will find that the further the balls have fallen, the more they will have been damaged by the impact with the floor. Gravity makes all four balls accelerate uniformly, but the ball that has fallen the greatest distance has had time to reach the greatest speed, and therefore will show the greatest damage.	QCA Unit 6E 'Forces in action'. Builds on Unit 4E 'Friction'. NC Sc4 (2) Forces and motion.	ES Energy and forces: Forces and their effects – Level D	AT4 Level 4/5
page 119	Bending light	To understand that we see things clearly when light is reflected off them straight into our eyes.	Lenses depend on light changing direction as it passes through them (refraction). This effect can be explored by looking at an object through a 'water lens', which the children can alter themselves. Visually impaired children may need support for this activity.	QCA Unit 6F 'How we see things'. Builds on Unit 3F 'Light and shadows' and Unit 5E 'Earth, Sun and Moon'. NC Sc4 (3) Light and sound.	ES Energy and forces: Properties and uses of energy – Level D	AT4 Level 4
page 120	The senses: sight	To begin to understand that different coloured light can deceive the eye.	It will be important to discuss the findings because children will be affected in different ways. They should find that the house disappears when seen through red Cellophane; there will be an after-image (probably blue) around the second figure (on the right); the lines are the same length. Visually impaired children may need support for this activity.	QCA Unit 6F 'How we see things'. Builds on Unit 3F 'Light and shadows' and Unit 5E 'Earth, Sun and Moon'. NC Sc4 (3) Light and sound.	ES Energy and forces: Properties and uses of energy – Level E	AT4 Level 4/5
page 121	See-through or not see-through	To know that light is blocked and changed by different materials.	You will need to collect as many materials as possible that are transparent, opaque and translucent. This activity should lead the children to understand that the opaque nature of materials forms shadows by blocking light. Visually impaired children may need support for this activity.	QCA Unit 6F 'How we see things'. Builds on Unit 3F 'Light and shadows' and Unit 5E 'Earth, Sun and Moon'. NC Sc4 (3) Light and sound.	ES Energy and forces: Properties and uses of energy – Level E	AT4 Level 4/5
page 122	Reflections	To understand that light from an object can be reflected by a mirror.	It is important that there are enough mirrors for each child. This activity will enable children to understand that the mirror image that they draw is the same distance behind the mirror as the object in front and that it is laterally inverted. Visually impaired children may need support for this activity.	QCA Unit 6F 'How we see things'. Builds on Unit 3F 'Light and shadows' and Unit 5E 'Earth, Sun and Moon'. NC Sc4 (3) Light and sound.	ES Energy and forces: Properties and uses of energy – Level C	AT4 Level 4
page 123	DANGER – Electricity!	To relate knowledge of electricity to familiar phenomena.	Many of the issues on this sheet should be discussed with the whole class. The picture contains most of the classic dangers associated with electricity in and around the home. The children could develop this discussion by making safety posters based on one or more of the features in the picture.	QCA Unit 6G 'Changing circuits'. Builds on Units 2F 'Using electricity' and Unit 4F 'Circuits and conductors'. NC Sc4 (1) Electricity.	ES Energy and forces: Property and uses of energy – Level D	AT4 Level 4/5
page 124	Electric motor	To complete an investigation relating to electrical circuits.	Make sure all the batteries, motors and bulbs are working before starting this activity. If the battery terminals or the motor terminals are reversed, then the motor will turn in the opposite direction. Two batteries will increase the speed and power of the motor, while the addition of a bulb will increase the resistance in the circuit and thus slow or stop the motor. A pencil lead will also increase electrical resistance.	QCA Unit 6G 'Changing circuits'. Builds on Units 2F 'Using electricity' and Unit 4F 'Circuits and conductors'. NC Sc4 (1) Electricity.	ES Energy and forces: Property and uses of energy – Level D	AT4 Level 4/5
page 125	Clown's face	To understand complete circuits and that switches can be used to control devices.	This model uses electrical circuits. It is important that the children draw the circuits after they have completed each model using conventional symbols. A variety of switches can be used to light up the bulbs, and a buzzer could be added.	QCA Unit 6G 'Changing circuits'. Builds on Units 2F 'Using electricity' and Unit 4F 'Circuits and conductors'. NC Sc4 (1) Electricity.	ES Energy and forces: Property and uses of energy – Level D	AT4 Level 4/5
page 126	Wheel of fortune	To understand complete circuits and that switches can be used to control devices.	This model uses electrical circuits. It is important that the children draw the circuits after they have completed each model using conventional symbols. By using a switch, the arrow can be made to spin. Secure the arrow to a small plastic pulley wheel fitted to the motor's spindle.	QCA Unit 6G 'Changing circuits'. Builds on Units 2F 'Using electricity' and Unit 4F 'Circuits and conductors'. NC Sc4 (1) Electricity.	ES Energy and forces: Property and uses of energy – Level D	AT4 Level 4/5
page 127	Car-park barrier	To understand complete circuits and that switches can be used to control devices.	This model uses electrical circuits. It is important that the children draw the circuits after they have completed each model using conventional symbols. The electromagnetic effect of a current can be used to move parts of a device. When a current is flowing through the coiled wire in the model, the iron nail will be pulled down towards it, thus lifting the barrier.	QCA Unit 6G 'Changing circuits'. Builds on Units 2F 'Using electricity' and Unit 4F 'Circuits and conductors'. NC Sc4 (1) Electricity.	ES Energy and forces: Property and uses of energy – Level D	AT4 Level 4/5

Food for your meals

❖ Draw a line from each food to the correct part of the circle.

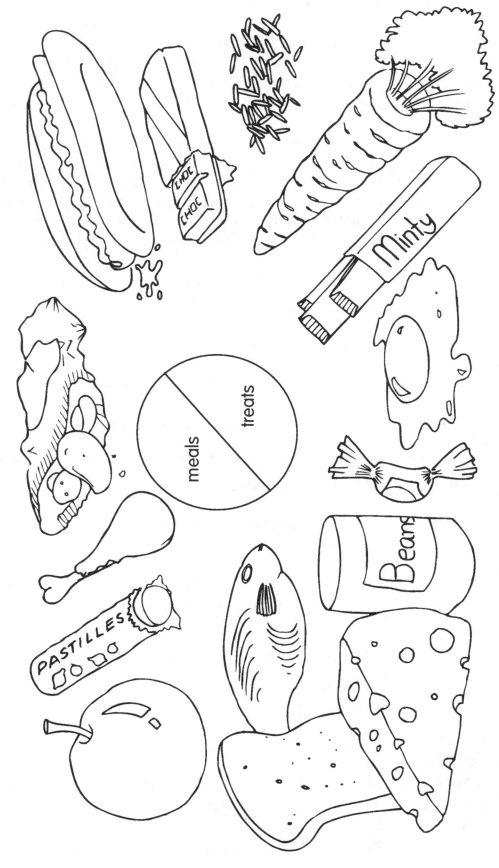

❖ Colour in red the foods you think have most sugar. What does sugar do to teeth?

A closer look at your food

✤ When do you get your nourishment?

✤ Think about your meals and tick the boxes in the table.

Meal	Action food **Carbohydrate** cereals, bread, potatoes, biscuits	Growth food **Protein** meat, fish, eggs, peas, cheese	Food for warmth **Fat** butter, cheese, milk, cream	Food for health **Vitamins and minerals** fruit and veg
Breakfast				
Snack				
Lunch				
Snack				
Tea				
Supper				

Does every meal have all the nutrients? _____

Do you eat food containing all the nutrients in a day? _____

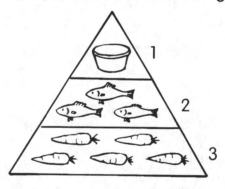

You should eat a little of fatty foods (1) a medium amount of protein foods (2) a large amount of foods with carbohydrates, vitamins and minerals (3).

✤ If you don't, how can you change your meals to healthier ones?

NO FUSS PHOTOCOPIABLE

SCHOLASTIC
www.scholastic.co.uk

Food for action and growth

The main foods for action are cereals and potatoes or foods which have sugar that makes them sweet. They contain energy-giving substances called carbohydrates.

♣ Write a C on each action food and draw a line to the runner.

The main foods for growth are meat, fish, eggs, cheese, milk, peas and beans. They contain body-building substances called proteins.

♣ Write a P on each body-building food and draw a line to the growing family.

Carbohydrates and proteins are called nutrients.

♣ Look on breakfast cereal packets for the words carbohydrates and protein. What other nutrient words do you find?

Food for warmth and health

Fatty foods give you energy and keep you warm.
Fat is a substance found in butter, cheese, cream, oily fish and margarines.

♣ Write an F on each fatty food and draw a line to the snow scene.

Vitamins and minerals keep you healthy. Most are found in cereals, fruit and vegetables.

♣ Write VM on each food you think contains vitamins and minerals and draw a line to the girl skipping.

♣ Write down the foods containing fat that you eat.

♣ Write down the foods containing vitamins and minerals that you eat.

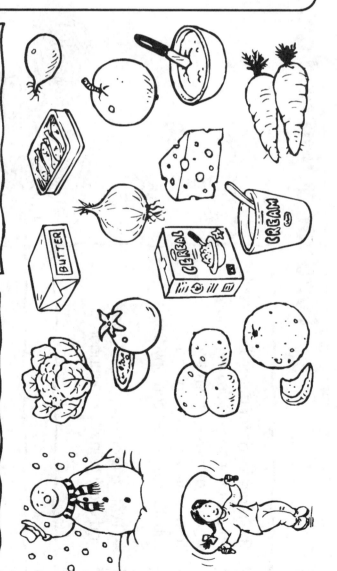

NO FUSS
PHOTOCOPIABLE

SCHOLASTIC
www.scholastic.co.uk

Name _____

Teeth and dental care

The average adult has 32 teeth and young children have 20 teeth. There are four different types of teeth and each type does a different job.

INCISORS – bite and cut food.
CANINES – hold and tear food.
PREMOLARS AND MOLARS – grind and crush food.

canine
incisor
premolar
molar

▲ Now see what you can find out about your own teeth.

How to clean your teeth

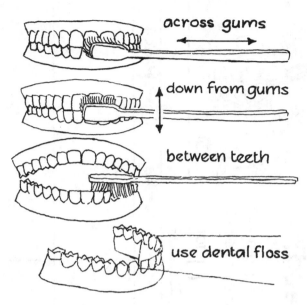

across gums

down from gums

between teeth

use dental floss

my teeth

▲ Using a hand mirror, count the number of teeth you have:

Upper jaw	Incisors	☐	Canines	☐	Premolars	☐	Molars	☐
Lower jaw	Incisors	☐	Canines	☐	Premolars	☐	Molars	☐

▲ How many fillings do you have?

▲ What do you like about your teeth?

▲ What don't you like?

▲ How many times do you visit the dentist in a year?

▲ Chew a disclosing tablet then use a mirror to see where the red patches are. This is where plaque gathers. Shade in where you can see plaque on your teeth on the diagram on the right.

▲ Plaque eats away at teeth and gums, so brush regularly!

What do plants need?

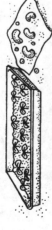

♣ Carry out this experiment to find out what plants need to grow strong and healthy. You will need: bean seeds, potting soil, sand, water, six pots. Plant the bean seeds under the following conditions and record what happens.

Condition	Prediction – will the beans grow?	Observations			
		Week 1	Week 2	Week 3	Week 4
potting soil water sunlight					
potting soil water in the dark					
potting soil no water sunlight					
potting soil no water in the dark					
sand water sunlight					
water sunlight					

NO FUSS PHOTOCOPIABLE

■ SCHOLASTIC
www.scholastic.co.uk

Name _____

✤ Draw what grows from the seed after a few days.

Can seeds grow any way up?

You will need:
a jar
blotting paper
soaked seeds
water

1 Set up a jar like this.

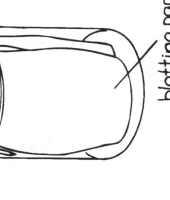

blotting paper

2 Put four seeds like this.

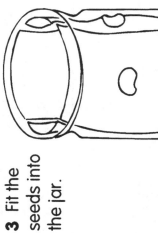

3 Fit the seeds into the jar.

Add water

■ SCHOLASTIC
www.scholastic.co.uk

Name _____

How plants change

You will need: bean seeds; plant pot; soil.

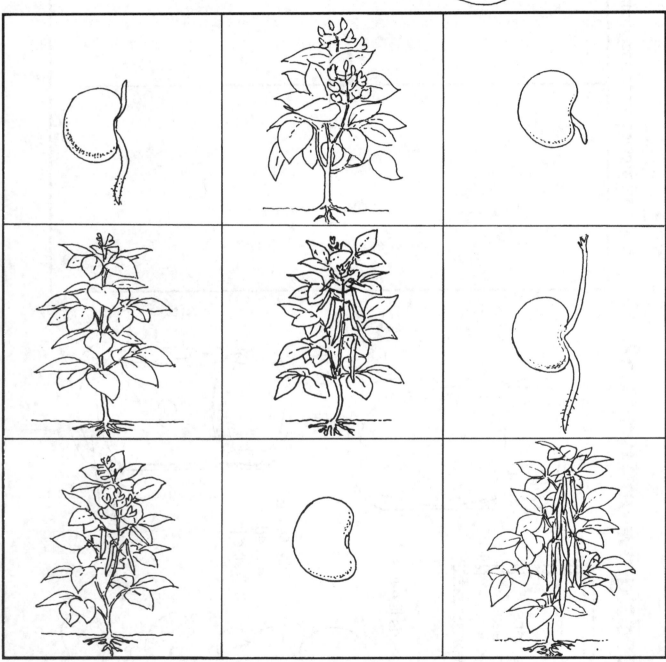

▲ How do plants change as they grow? Look at the pictures of a bean plant above. Cut out the pictures and place them in the correct order. Share you result with others. Do they agree?

▲ Plant some bean seeds in a plant pot in the classroom. Water when needed. Make a record of the plants' changes as they grow.

SCHOLASTIC
www.scholastic.co.uk

Name _____

Bean seedlings

You will need: broad beans; potting compost; three yoghurt pots; water; pencil; paper.

Nadeem and Paul carried out an experiment on growing bean seeds. They got three yoghurt pots and filled them with potting compost. They placed a bean seed inside each pot. They watered the compost when it was dry. They placed one pot in the fridge, one in a cool, dark place and one in a warm, sunny place.

This is what the bean seedlings looked like after four weeks:

1   What do you think Nadeem and Paul were trying to find out? _____

_____

2   Why do you think the plant did not grow in the fridge? _____

_____

3   Explain why the plant in the cool, dark place grew spindly and yellow.

_____

4   Why did the plant grow best in a warm, sunny place? _____

_____

▲ Now try out this experiment yourself. Keep a diary of what happens. How do your results compare with Nadeem and Paul's investigation?

▲ Try the same experiment with different seed types. How do the results compare?

Name _____

Materials all around

You will need: a pencil; a clipboard.
If you look around, you will see many different materials being used.

▲ Do three surveys. Look for things made of plastic, rock, metal, wood, fabric, paper, rubber and glass. Write their names in the table.

Materials	Survey 1 Things I can touch without leaving my seat	Survey 2 Things I can find around the classroom	Survey 3 Things I can see when standing in the playground
plastic			
rock			
metal			
wood			
fabric			
paper			
rubber			
glass			

▲ Which materials seem to be the most common?
▲ Which category of material was the most difficult to find?
▲ Make a collection of each type of material. Display and label your collections.

SCHOLASTIC
www.scholastic.co.uk

Marvellous metals

You will need: wax crayons; pencils; paper.

▲ Collect as many of these metal objects as you can.
Decide why metal was used to make each object.
Could it have been made of any other material?

nail	key	piece of wire
paperclip	aluminium dish	1kg weight
drinks can	silver necklace	scissors
coin	bell	spoon

Metal object	Why metal was used	What other material could be used?
nail	It's strong and can be made sharp	none

▲ Make a list of all the things you have found out about metals.
Metals can be moulded into detailed shapes and patterns.
▲ Use pencils and crayons to make rubbings of metal objects
such as coins or keys. Use these to make a decorative collage.

Name _____

Wonderful wood

You will need: a hand lens; pencils; wax crayons; paper.

▲ Make a collection of pieces of wood and objects made of wood. Use a hand lens to examine each one. Write down everything you notice about the appearance, pattern and texture of wood.

▲ You will find wood is used for all kinds of purposes. Can you find examples where wood is important in these situations?

in building houses	**for sports equipment**
in art and craft activities	**in your bedroom**
for kitchen equipment	**for a method of transport**

▲ Record your ideas in the table.

Situation	Where wood is used	Why wood is used
Building houses		
Kitchen equipment		
Art and craft activities		
Transport		
Sports equipment		
Bedroom		

▲ Wood and weather: look around and find out what happens to wood outside. Examine dead branches and old doors and window frames. Write down your observations. Do some sketches.

You will have found different patterns and textures in wood.
▲ Use pencils and crayons to make rubbings and create a decorative collage.

www.scholastic.co.uk

Name _____

Useful plastic

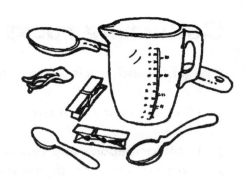

You will need: a collection of plastic items; some of the same items in different materials; a pencil; paper.

There are about 30 different types of plastic in general use.
▲ Collect ten plastic items that you use every day.
Examine them carefully and tick their properties in this table.

Name of item	thin	firm	transparent	can be folded	light in weight	waterproof	breakable	long-lasting

▲ Now find two items, one made of plastic and the other made of a different material, which both have the same use, like the examples below.

plastic and wooden clothes pegs
plastic and metal spoons
plastic and glass jugs

▲ Compare the two items, writing down the good points and bad points about each.

Getting rid of plastic can be difficult. Rubbish is often buried.

▲ Bury some different types of plastic in the ground together with some pieces of paper and wood. Examine them every week and record what happens to them.

Name _____

Collecting rocks

You will need: labels and a hand-lens.

▲ Make a collection of rocks.

I Look for pebbles and pieces of rock in the garden, at the seaside, by the roadside and in the country.

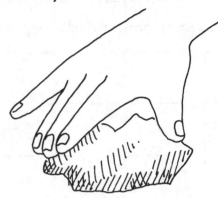

2 Wash your rocks and pebbles carefully and then dry them.

3 Label each one with the place and date on which you found it.

4 Look at each pebble carefully using a hand-lens.

- What colour is it?
- Is it rough or smooth to the touch?
- Does it appear to be made of grains?
- Is it made of crystals?

▲ Write your observations in the chart below. Use books to try to find the names of your rocks.

rock	colour	rough	smooth	grains	crystals

SCHOLASTIC
www.scholastic.co.uk

Name _____

Comparing rocks

You will need: a small collection of rocks; a hand-lens; a 2p coin and a nail.

▲ Look carefully at each of your rocks.

▲ What does each one feel like?

_____

_____

_____

_____

_____

▲ Devise a test to find out which of your rocks is hardest and which is softest. You could use your fingernail, a 2p coin and a nail. Make a record of your results.

▲ What does each rock smell like?

_____

_____

_____

_____

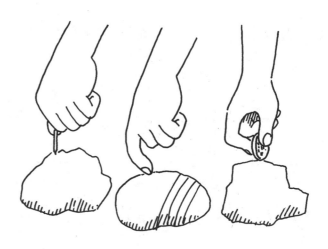

▲ Now arrange your rocks in order of hardness.

▲ What does each rock look like when it is wet?

_____

_____

_____

_____

_____

▲ How many words can you think of to describe each rock?

SCHOLASTIC
www.scholastic.co.uk

NO FUSS
PHOTOCOPIABLE

Name _____

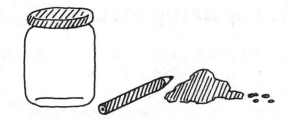

What does soil consist of?

You will need: a pencil; a clear plastic jar with a lid; soil and water.

▲ Do this experiment to investigate what soil is made of.

1 Put some soil in the jar.

2 Three-quarter fill the jar with water.

3 Put the lid on and shake the jar hard.

4 Leave the soil to settle for a few days. What happens to it?

_____

_____

_____

_____

▲ How many layers can you see?

_____

_____

5 Now try other soils from different places. Are they all the same?

☐ **yes**   ☐ **no**

(tick the correct box)

▲ How can you make your tests fair?

■ SCHOLASTIC
www.scholastic.co.uk

Name _____

Make a model mountain

You will need: a garden and a watering can.

1 Make a mudpie mountain in the garden. Be sure to pat the mud down smoothly.

2 Push some large stones into the mud and then let it dry hard.

3 Draw your mountain in the box below.

▲ Where do rivers, streams and waterfalls form on your mountain?

_____

_____

▲ Are any valleys formed? What shape are they?

_____

_____

▲ Where does mud which is eroded from the mountain finish up?

_____

_____

▲ Draw your eroded mudpie mountain.

4 Water your mountain with a watering can and watch carefully.

▲ In which places does the water wash away, or erode, your mountain?

_____

_____

_____

NO FUSS PHOTOCOPIABLE

Name _____

Changes in the landscape

Erosion is the name given to the process where land is worn away. Erosion is caused by water, wind and ice. Over time, the landscape can change greatly due to this wearing away.

▲ Look at the diagrams below. Decide how the land has been worn away. Look at the landscape features produced. Decide how they may have been formed. Use reference books to help you.

Landscape features		Your comments
1. before [image]	after [image]	Type of erosion _____
2. before [image]	after [image]	Type of erosion_____
3. before [image]	after [image]	Type of erosion _____

▲ Look at landscape features in your area. Decide how they were formed.

NO FUSS
PHOTOCOPIABLE

SCHOLASTIC
www.scholastic.co.uk

Making a magnet

YOU WILL NEED
- soft iron nails;
- a bar magnet;
- some paper clips;
- other classroom objects.

❖ Take a soft iron nail and stroke it with the magnet in the same direction 30 times.

❖ Test the nail's magnetic power using some paper clips.

❖ How long does the nail keep its magnetism? _____

❖ Try to magnetise other objects. Describe what happens below.

Name _____

Magnetic forces

You will need: two bar magnets, the objects listed below.

▲ Which of these things will be attracted to a magnet?

Predict first, then use your magnet to see if you were right.

▲ Record your results on the chart below.

Object	Prediction	Result
2p coin		
10p coin		
ruler		
eraser		
nail		
paper		
paper-clip		
plastic lid		
glass jar		
pin		
pencil		
elastic band		

▲ Discuss your results with a friend. What materials do you think are magnetic?

When two magnets pull towards each other, they are said to **attract**.
When two magnets push each other away, they are send to **repel** each other.

▲ Find out what happens when you try each of these:

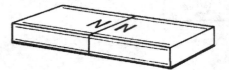

Two North poles adjacent: repel or attract? _____

North and South pole adjacent: repel or attract? _____

South and North poles adjacent: repel or attract? _____

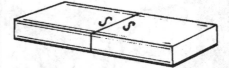

Two South poles adjacent: repel or attract? _____

▲ Summarise what you have discovered by completing this sentence:

Unlike poles —————————, whereas like poles —————————.

NO FUSS
PHOTOCOPIABLE

■SCHOLASTIC
www.scholastic.co.uk

Name _____

How strong is a magnet?

You will need: a box of paper-clips; bar magnets of several different sizes; adhesive tape.

▲ Carry out this experiment to find out how strong your magnet is.

1. Tape one of the magnets to a table, making sure that part of the magnet sticks over the edge of the table.
2. Bend open the end of a paper-clip to make a hook. Touch this hook to the end of the magnet that is over the edge of the table.
3. Add other paper-clips one at a time to the paper-clip hook.

• How many paper-clips can you add before they pull loose from the magnet and fall?

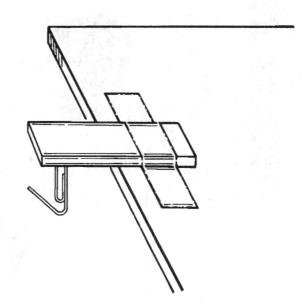

▲ Repeat this activity with other magnets of different sizes.

• Which is the strongest magnet? Is it the largest one?

▲ Are the two ends of a magnet equally strong? Find out.

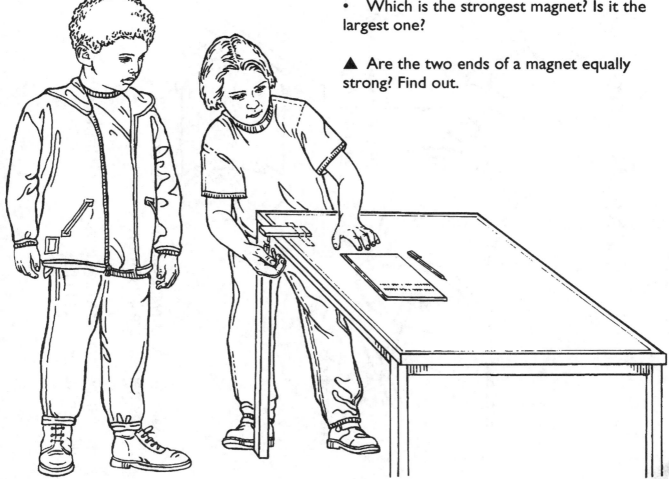

■ SCHOLASTIC
www.scholastic.co.uk

NO FUSS PHOTOCOPIABLE

Cotton reel crawler

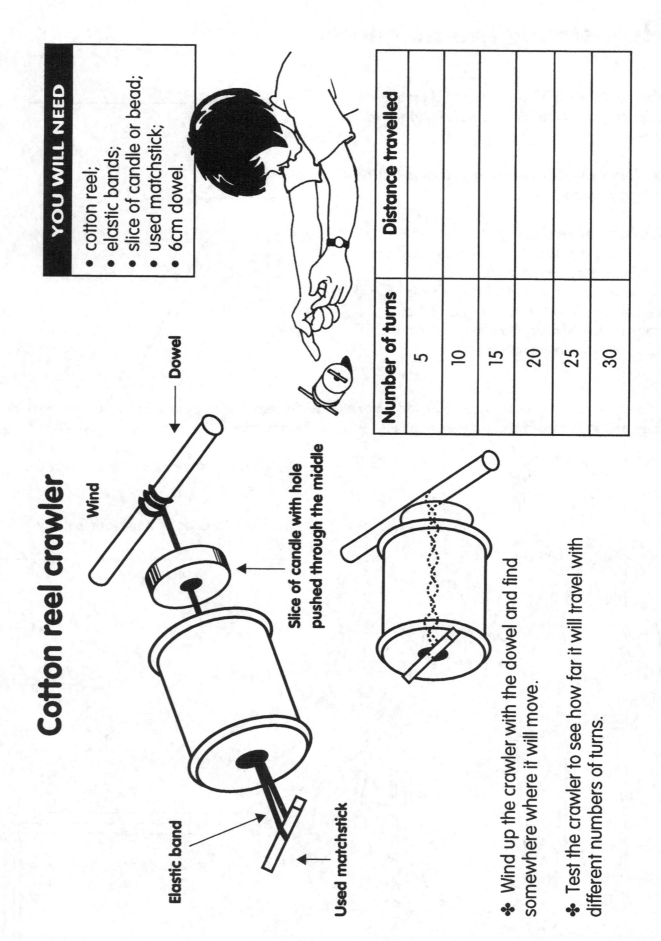

YOU WILL NEED

- cotton reel;
- elastic bands;
- slice of candle or bead;
- used matchstick;
- 6cm dowel.

Dowel

Wind

Slice of candle with hole pushed through the middle

Elastic band

Used matchstick

Number of turns	Distance travelled
5	
10	
15	
20	
25	
30	

❧ Wind up the crawler with the dowel and find somewhere where it will move.

❧ Test the crawler to see how far it will travel with different numbers of turns.

NO FUSS PHOTOCOPIABLE

SCHOLASTIC
www.scholastic.co.uk

Name _____

What causes night and day?

You will need: a pencil; a globe or a large ball; a desk lamp or a torch.

▲ Conduct this experiment in a darkened room to see what causes night and day.

1. Stand the globe or ball on the table.

2. Shine the light on to it, as shown in the picture below.

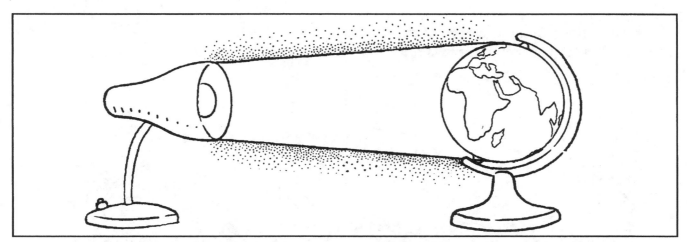

3. Pretend the lamp or torch is the Sun.
- Which part of the globe is light?
- Which part is dark?
- Draw what you see.

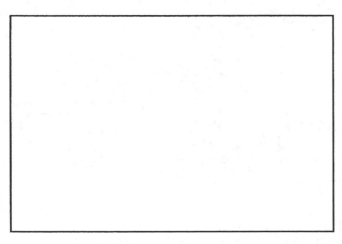

▲ What causes day and night?

_____

_____

4. Slowly turn the globe or ball. Draw what you see now.

▲ Make a list of some of the places which have their night-time when it is daytime where you live.

_____

_____

_____

■SCHOLASTIC
www.scholastic.co.uk

Name _____

What colour is sunlight?

You will need: a pencil; a shallow tray of water; a small mirror.

Do this activity on a sunny day. Do not reflect light into anyone's eyes.

▲ Sunlight looks white. But is it really white?

1. Stand the tray of water near a sunny window-sill.

2. Rest the mirror on the edge of the tray so that the mirror is partly under water.

3. Gently move the mirror.

4. Can you see colours reflected on the wall or ceiling?

• What colours are they?

_____

_____

_____

• Where else have you seen these colours?

_____

_____

_____

■ SCHOLASTIC
www.scholastic.co.uk

Name _____

Tracking shadows

You will need: a piece of chalk.

▲ Do this activity on a sunny day to find out what happens to your shadow. Work with a friend.

1. First thing in the morning, stand in the playground.

2. Ask your friend to draw around your shoes. Then ask your friend to draw around your shadow.

3. Stand in the same place an hour later.

4. Ask your friend to draw around your shadow again. Do this every hour.

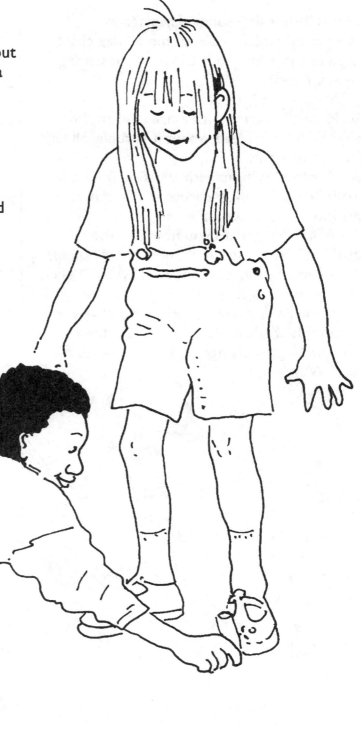

▲ Does your shadow stay in the same place? If it doesn't, what made it move?

_____

_____

_____

SCHOLASTIC
www.scholastic.co.uk

Shadows

You will need: a sunny day, place in playground which receives sun all day, chalk, large nail in a flat piece of wood, measuring tape, a pencil.

▲ Place the board with a nail in it on the playground in a place where it is sunny all day. Do not move it.

▲ Once every hour, visit the site. Trace the shadow with chalk. Measure the length of the shadow. Record the time and length.

▲ What changes do you notice in the shadows? Why did the shadow move round? When was the shadow shortest? Why? When was the shadow longest? Why does the length of shadow change? How effective would this shadow clock be? Would the shadow lengths change at different times of year? Why?

Time	Length of shadow

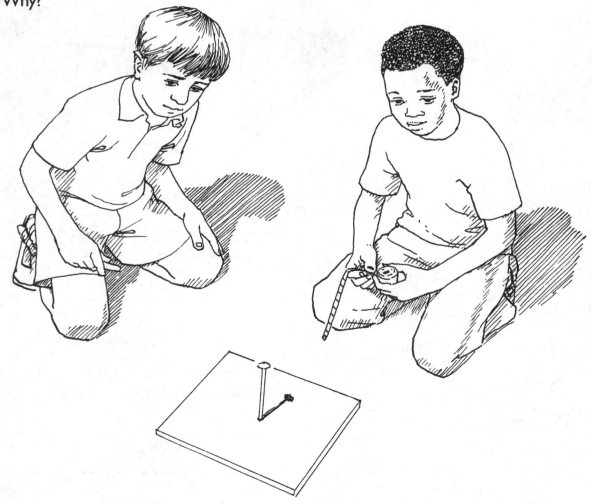

NO FUSS
PHOTOCOPIABLE

SCHOLASTIC
www.scholastic.co.uk

The skeleton

▲ Look at the wordlist in the box. Can you find the correct name of each bone labelled on this diagram? Use reference books to help you and write your answers in the correct spaces.

| breast bone |
| shoulder blade |
| lower arm |
| thigh bone |
| hip bone |
| lower arm |
| back bone |
| collar bone |
| rib |
| upper arm |
| skull |
| finger bones |
| lower leg |
| knee cap |
| lower leg |
| foot bones |

▲ Can you find out the medical names for these bones?
▲ Find out how many bones there are in your body.

Name _____

The joints

You will need: card; a pencil; a paper-fastener; scissors and glue.

Joints are where one bone joins another bone. Most joints allow bones to move. There are two main types of joints:

Ball and socket

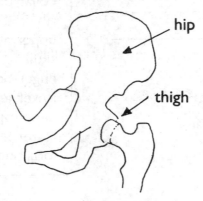

hip

thigh

Hinge

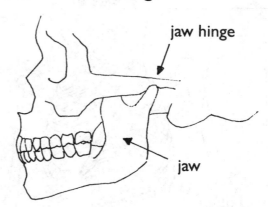

jaw hinge

jaw

▲ Make a model skull showing a hinge joint.

1 Trace the shapes of the skull below or cut them out and glue them on to card.
2 Fix a paper-fastener through the 'x' on each piece to join the jaw to the skull.

▲ Does it move like your jaw?
▲ Can you name other bones which have ball and socket or hinge joints?

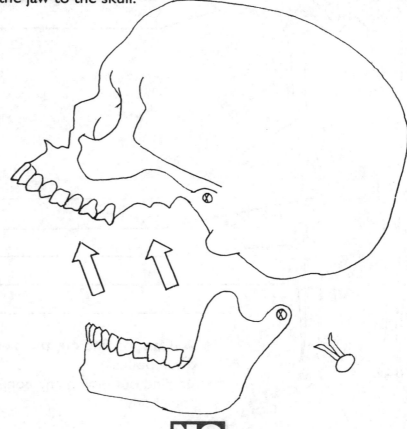

NO FUSS
PHOTOCOPIABLE

SCHOLASTIC
www.scholastic.co.uk

Name _____

The muscles

You will need: strong card; scissors; three elastic bands and a paper-fastener.

Muscles help our body move. There are over 600 muscles in our body and they are joined to our bones with tendons. They work in pairs so that each movement can be reversed. For example: the biceps in your arm flex your arm and the triceps extend it.

▲ Make a model 'hand'.

1 Cut out shapes A and B below. Glue them on to thick card and cut them out again.
2 Join the two pieces of card together with the paper-fastener and elastic bands.
3 When you move the handles together, the 'fingers' open. Watch how the bands stretch and contract like your muscles. Try to pick up objects with your 'hand'.

▲ Can you design a model arm or leg which moves?

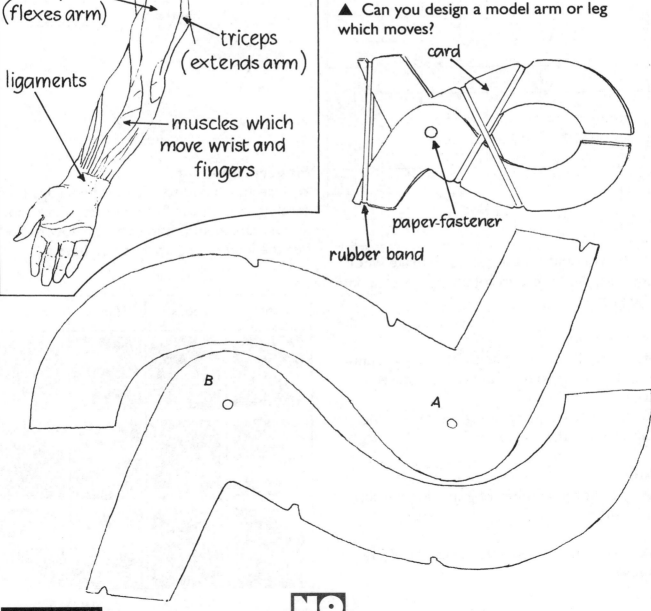

biceps (flexes arm)

triceps (extends arm)

ligaments

muscles which move wrist and fingers

card

paper-fastener

rubber band

B

A

■SCHOLASTIC
www.scholastic.co.uk

NO FUSS
PHOTOCOPIABLE

Name _____

Hands

You will need: a ruler; an ink pad; 1 cm squared paper; string; measuring tape; plain paper and a pencil.

▲ Carry out these activities to discover all you can about your hands.

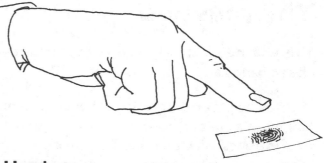

Area
▲ Trace your hand on to squared paper.
▲ Put an 'x' in all the whole squares and count the total.

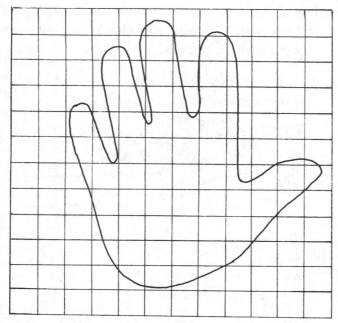

▲ Now count up the halves to make whole squares. Add the two totals together to find the area.

Perimeters
▲ Carefully place a length of string around the outline of your hand on the squared paper.
▲ Stretch the string along the measuring tape to find the total length.

Joints
▲ Count the number of joints in your fingers and thumb.

▲ Now record your results for all of the above.

Handspans
▲ Stretch your hand out as wide as it will go. Measure the distance between the tip of the little finger and the thumb. This is your handspan.

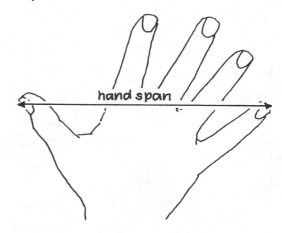

hand span

Fingerprints
▲ Use an ink pad to ink your fingertips then carefully press your fingers on to white paper.
▲ Use the identification chart below to find out the kind of fingerprints you have.

Arches	Loops	Whorls	Composites

NO FUSS PHOTOCOPIABLE

SCHOLASTIC
www.scholastic.co.uk

Name _____

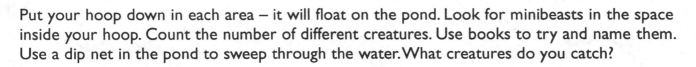

Minibeast sampling

You will need: a hoop; a hand lens; a dip net; a pencil; reference books on minibeasts to help with identification.

▲ Compare the minibeasts found in three different areas:

A a rocky place;
B a grassy place;
C a pond.

Put your hoop down in each area – it will float on the pond. Look for minibeasts in the space inside your hoop. Count the number of different creatures. Use books to try and name them. Use a dip net in the pond to sweep through the water. What creatures do you catch?

▲ Complete the table below for each area.

Area	Number found	Names of minibeasts found	Drawing of one minibeast
rocky place			
grassy place			
pond			

▲ Find out more information about one minibeast in each area. What special features do they have which help them to live in each place?

www.scholastic.co.uk

Pond survey

▲ Name _____ Date _____

You will need: a pond net; a plastic container; a pencil; paper; a clipboard.

▲ Different animals live in different parts of a pond. Do this survey to find out which animals live at the surface, the middle and the bottom of a pond.

Sweep the net along the surface of the pond several times. Record what you find in the table. Do the same for the middle and lower depths of the pond.

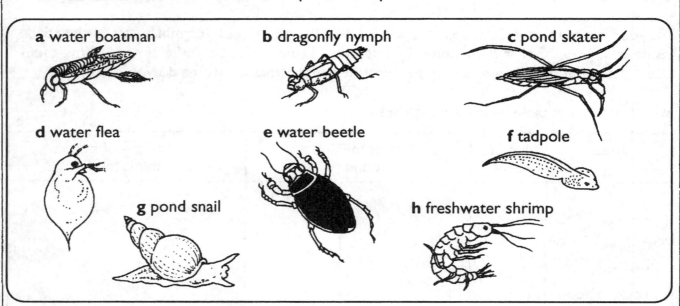

a water boatman   **b** dragonfly nymph   **c** pond skater

d water flea   **e** water beetle   **f** tadpole

g pond snail   **h** freshwater shrimp

▲ Tick the animals you find in each area.

Pond area	Animal								Other animals (write name)	
	a	b	c	d	e	f	g	h		
surface										
middle										
bottom										

▲ Draw a picture of an animal from each area of the pond on some paper.

▲ Compare what you found with others.

▲ Find out more about some of these animals.

NO FUSS PHOTOCOPIABLE

Name _____

Plant habitats

You will need: a pencil; clipboard; plant reference books.

▲ Visit a meadow and complete the chart about the plants which grow there.

▲ Next visit a wood and complete another chart about the plants you find there. Compare your findings with others.

Habitat: _____
Tick the plants which grow in this area: trees ☐ grass ☐ mosses ☐ shrubs ☐ fungi ☐ liverworts ☐ flowers ☐ ferns ☐
What is the main kind of plant? _____ What is the name of this plant? _____ Draw two plants you find here:
What is the tallest plant in this area? _____ Estimate its height. _____ What is the shortest plant in this area? _____ Estimate its height. _____ Describe one of the plants you find.

▲ Visit two other sites such as scrubland, a pond, moor or wasteland. Compare the plants found in each site.

www.scholastic.co.uk

Name _____

What is there living under cover?

You will need:
magnifying glass

* With an adult: look under stones, bricks, logs and leaves for small animals. Tally or write down the number you find every time you turn something over.
* Use the table to help you.

* At the end of the hunt add up the numbers for each animal. Which animal do you find most of?

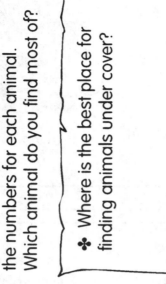

* Where is the best place for finding animals under cover?

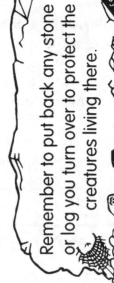

Remember to put back any stone or log you turn over to protect the creatures living there.

Animal		How many?	Total
woodlouse			
earthworm			
beetle			
earwig			
spider			
centipede			
millepede			
snail			
slug			

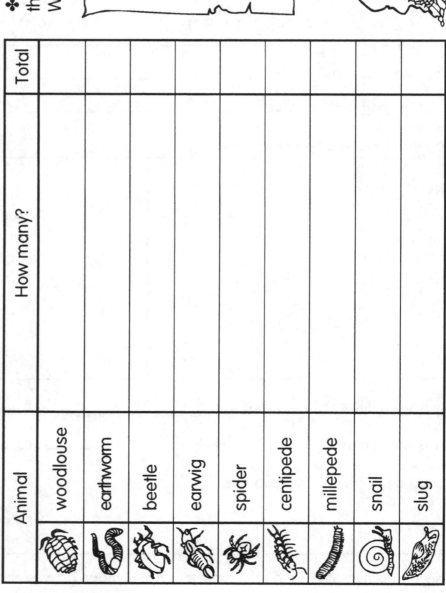

NO FUSS
PHOTOCOPIABLE

SCHOLASTIC
www.scholastic.co.uk

Name _____

Using pitfall traps

♣ Follow the instructions in the pictures.

You will need:
plastic jars, gravel, card squares, tray, stones

1 Dig out the soil.

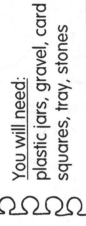

2 Put in the jar.

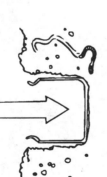

3 Fill in soil around the side.

4 Put four stones around the top.

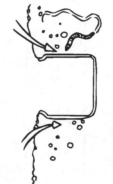

5 Put card over top.

6 Cover with stones and leaves.

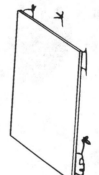

7 Leave overnight and empty the following morning.

8 Let the animals go.

♣ What did you find?

harvestman

rove beetle

ground beetle

spider

woodlouse

centipede

millipede

Name _____

Thermometers and temperature

You will need: a pencil; two thermometers.

Handle your thermometers carefully. Do this activity on a sunny day.

▲ Take the thermometers outside in the morning.

▲ Hang one thermometer on a wall outside your classroom where the sun can shine on it. Hang the other thermometer in the shade of a tree. Take the temperature from each thermometer every hour for a whole day.

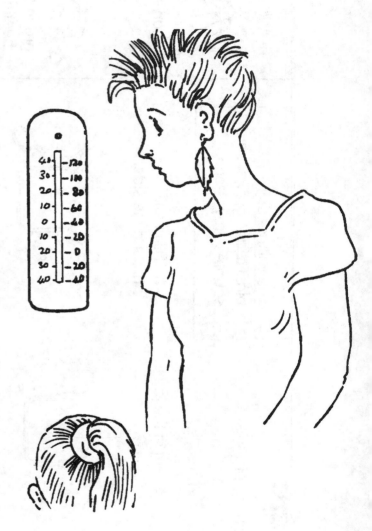

▲ Find the best way to record your results.

▲ Why do weather scientists always take the temperature in the shade?

_____

_____

▲ Take the temperature from the same place outside every day for a month.

• When is the highest temperature?

_____

• When is the lowest temperature?

_____

NO FUSS PHOTOCOPIABLE

Warming water with the Sun

You will need: a pencil, two plastic jars, both the same size; two thermometers; white paper; black paper.

Some people use the Sun to warm the water they use in their homes. The things they use to do this are called solar panels. You might have seen solar panels like these.

▲ Do this activity on a sunny day to investigate solar heating.

1. Put the same amount of cold water in both jars and stand them on a sunny window-sill.

2. Put black paper around one jar. Put white paper around the other jar.

3. Take the temperature of both lots of water.

4. Take the temperature again after an hour.

White jar

Black jar

▲ What would be the best colour for a solar panel, black or white?

_____

_____

▲ In which part of the world would solar power be (a) most useful; (b) least useful?

_____

_____

▲ What are the advantages of using solar energy to heat water? What are the disadvantages?

_____

_____

_____

_____

_____

Name _____

Travelling heat

You will need: a pencil; a collection of objects to test; supervised access to a hot radiator or sunny window sill; a freezer.

▲ Collect these objects for the tests.

a piece of card   **something plastic**
a cork   **a metal object**
a piece of fabric   **a piece of**
something wooden   **polystyrene**

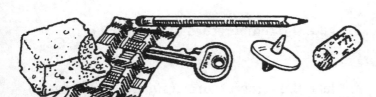

Heat is always trying to escape. It travels from hot spots to colder areas. Heat can travel through some materials more quickly than others.

▲ Find out which materials heat can travel through quickly. Use the chart to write down your results.

1 First, feel each object and decide whether it is hot, warm, cool or cold.
2 Put the objects in a warm place such as on a radiator or a sunny window sill.
3 After ten minutes, touch each object carefully and decide if there is any change.
4 Put the same objects in a freezer for ten minutes.
5 Quickly decide how they feel.

| Name of object | How it felt | | | ✗ ✓ |
	before the test	after being in a hot place	after being in a freezer	

▲ Put a tick next to the objects which quickly changed their temperatures.
▲ Put a cross next to the objects which hardly changed.

✓ These materials let heat pass through them easily. They are good conductors of heat.	✗ These materials did not let heat pass through them easily. They are good insulators of heat.

■SCHOLASTIC
www.scholastic.co.uk

Name _____

Keeping cool, staying warm

You will need: ice cubes; pieces of aluminium foil, newspaper, fabric, writing paper, cling-film; six small containers; tea cosy or something similar; hot water; two other containers.

 Take care when using hot liquids.

We often try to stop heat moving about. Sometimes we use materials to keep heat in, sometimes to keep heat out. The materials we choose are good *thermal insulators*.
▲ Find out which materials can stop heat reaching ice and melting it.
1 Quickly wrap each ice cube in a different material. You could use newspaper, writing paper, cling-film, aluminium foil and fabric.
2 Put each wrapped cube in its own container.
3 Put an unwrapped cube in a container too.

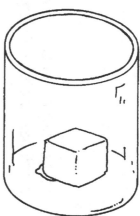

▲ Which ice cube was the first to melt?
▲ Which ice cube was the last to melt?
▲ Which material was the best at keeping the heat away from the ice – therefore the best thermal insulator?

▲ Does a tea cosy really work?
1 Ask an adult to fill two identical containers with hot water.
2 Carefully place a tea cosy, a woolly hat or a piece of fabric over one container.
3 Leave the containers for 15 minutes.
4 Very carefully feel the sides of the containers.

▲ Is there any difference in temperature?

SCHOLASTIC
www.scholastic.co.uk

NO FUSS
PHOTOCOPIABLE

Name _____

Cooling a hot drink

The pictures below show the same cup of hot chocolate as it cools down.

❖ Write the correct temperature in each small box and fill in the graph.

❖ What would you predict the temperature of the drink to be after 25 minutes?

[ ] °C

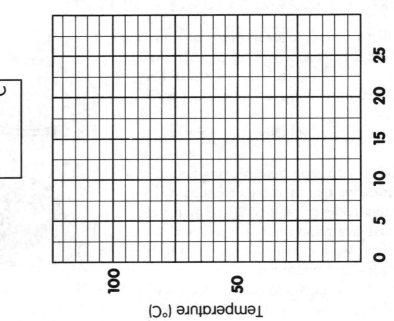

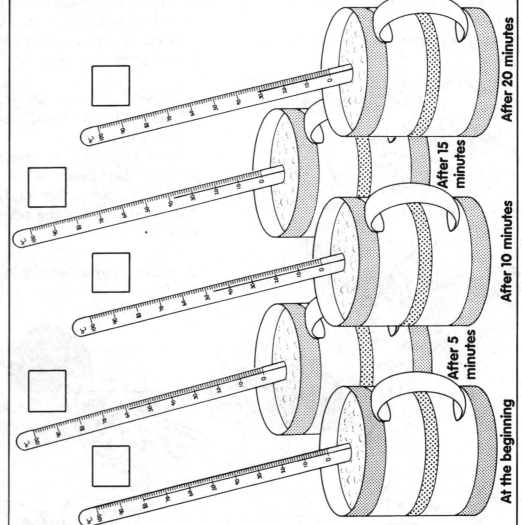

NO FUSS PHOTOCOPIABLE

SCHOLASTIC
www.scholastic.co.uk

Name _____

Dissolving things

You will need: jam jars; water; sugar; salt; pepper; flour; scouring powder; bicarbonate of soda; spoon.

1 Fill a jar with water.
2 Add one spoonful of salt.
3 Stir.
4 Does the salt dissolve?

▲ Try out the other ingredients. Predict the result first then record what happens.

▲ Does the water change colour?

Substance	Prediction – will it dissolve?	Result
sugar		
salt		
pepper		
flour		
scouring powder		
bicarbonate of soda		

▲ What affects whether something dissolves or not?
▲ Do fine substances dissolve better than coarse ones? Try different types of sugar.
▲ Does it help to stir the water?
▲ Will heating the water affect how things dissolve?
▲ Which substance dissolves the fastest? Why do you think this is?

Name _____

Changing colours

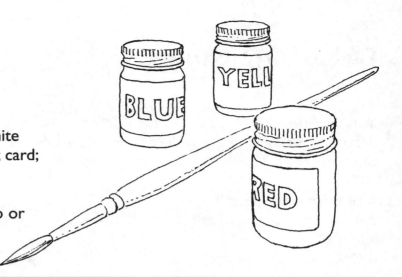

You will need: red, blue, yellow and white paint (or cellophane); paper; paint brush; card; felt-tipped pens; matchstick.

You can make different colours using two or three other colours mixed together.
▲ Try out these mixes:

Colour mix	Prediction – what colour will it make?	Result – what colour did it make?
blue and yellow		
red and yellow		
red and blue		
red, blue and yellow		
blue and white		
red and white		
yellow and white		

▲ How many different shades of each colour can you make?
▲ Can you make black?

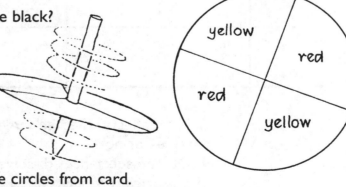

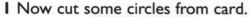

1 Now cut some circles from card.
2 Colour as shown with felt-tipped pens.
3 Make a hole in the centre for a matchstick.
4 Spin the cards quickly. What happens?

▲ Try different colours and patterns. Record the results.

SCHOLASTIC
www.scholastic.co.uk

Name _____

Solids, liquids and gases

A **solid** is something which usually does not change its shape, for example, a rock, sugar. A **liquid** is something which can flow from one place to another, for example, water, milk. A **gas** cannot usually be seen. It fills the whole space it is in, for example, the air around us.

▲ Look at the objects below. Decide whether each is a solid, liquid or gas.

▲ Make a list of the solids, liquids and gases in your classroom. Share your list with others. Do they agree?

butter	honey	wood	bubbles in soft drink
inside a balloon	salt	ice lolly	candle
ketchup	paper	steam	nail

■SCHOLASTIC
www.scholastic.co.uk

NO FUSS
PHOTOCOPIABLE

Name _____

Physical and chemical changes

When we change the appearance of something without turning it into something else we are making a *physical change*, such as bending a nail or freezing water to make ice.

When we change something into something else we are making a *chemical change*, such as burning wood to make charcoal or smelting iron to make steel.

▲ Look at the following changes. Decide if there has been a physical or chemical change made. Discuss your decision with others. Do they agree?

▲ Make a list of physical and chemical changes which can be made at home or at school.

ice lolly	melted ice lolly	milk	yoghurt

type of change: | type of change:

wood	wood sawn in half	can	squashed can

type of change: | type of change:

flour, water, salt, yeast	bread	saucepan of milk	heated milk

type of change: | type of change:

NO FUSS
PHOTOCOPIABLE

SCHOLASTIC
www.scholastic.co.uk

Name _____

Feeling forces

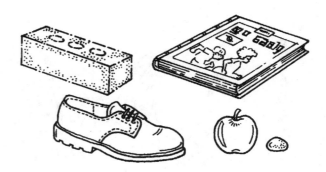

You will need: a collection of small objects such as an apple, a book, a shoe, a pebble and a brick; a scarf or a blindfold.

▲ Conduct this experiment to see if you can 'feel' forces. Work with a friend.

1. Close your eyes or ask your friend to blindfold you.
2. Ask your friend to arrange the objects in a row in front of you.
3. Pick up the objects one at a time and 'feel' the force each one makes.

▲ In which direction are these forces acting?

4. Now try to arrange the objects in order from the biggest force to the smallest. Remove your blindfold then write down this order of objects.
5. Now blindfold your friend.
6. Rearrange the objects in a different order.
7. Ask your friend to feel each force and to arrange the objects in order.

▲ Is your friend's order the same as yours?   ▲ How can you check to see who is right?

www.scholastic.co.uk

NO FUSS
PHOTOCOPIABLE

Name _____

Friction – friend or foe?

The force called friction can be helpful or a nuisance. Each of the pictures below shows the friction force with an arrow.

✤ In the small boxes provided, label each example as **H** for **helpful** or **N** for **nuisance**.

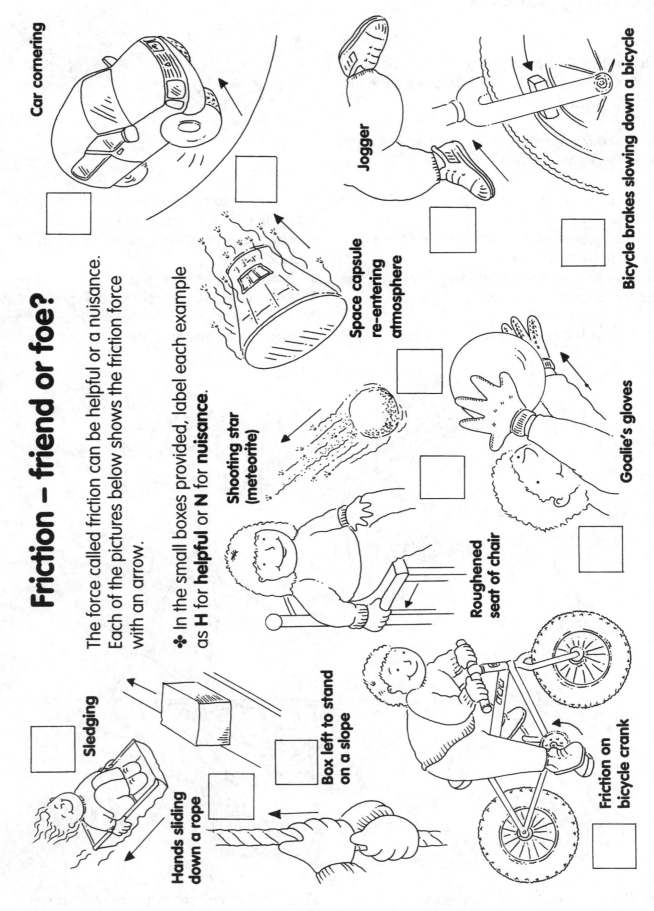

Car cornering

Jogger

Bicycle brakes slowing down a bicycle

Space capsule re-entering atmosphere

Shooting star (meteorite)

Goalie's gloves

Roughened seat of chair

Sledging

Box left to stand on a slope

Hands sliding down a rope

Friction on bicycle crank

NO FUSS
PHOTOCOPIABLE

SCHOLASTIC
www.scholastic.co.uk

Name _____

The effect of rubber on friction?

You will need: a small piece of wood, about 14cm by 7cm; a ruler or tape measure; some thick elastic bands; a small hook or screw eye; a spring balance or force meter; a heavy book.

▲ Conduct the following experiment to see what effect rubber has on friction.

1. Screw the hook into the end of the piece of wood.
2. Lay the piece of wood on a smooth table.
3. Fix the hook of the spring balance or force meter to the hook in the wood.
4. What force is needed to make the piece of wood begin to slide along the table? Record your result.

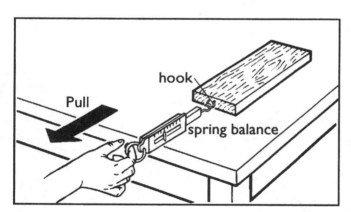

5. Now put three elastic bands around the piece of wood. Use the balance or force meter to see what force is needed to move the piece of wood now. Is it more or less than before?

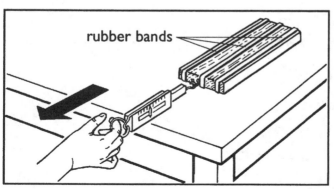

6. Repeat the experiment with a heavy book resting on the piece of wood. Pull the piece of wood along, with and without the elastic bands on it.

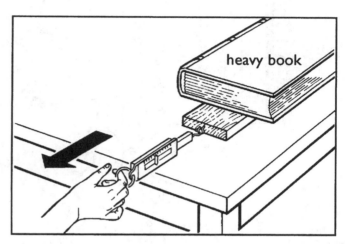

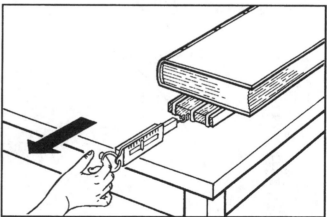

▲ When is the most force needed to move the wood?

▲ Do elastic bands increase or decrease friction?

▲ What happens if you do the experiment with a large stone or a house brick on the piece of wood?

▲ How many ways can you think of in which rubber is used because of the effects it has on friction?

Name _____

Parachute design

YOU WILL NEED

- scissors;
- thread;
- sticky tape;
- Plasticine;
- two copies of this worksheet.

❖ Carefully cut out the shape opposite.

❖ Use it to make a parachute.

❖ Compare the way it falls against a parachute which does **not** have a hole in it (made from the second worksheet).

❖ Does the hole make a difference?

Cut out here.

NO FUSS
PHOTOCOPIABLE

■SCHOLASTIC
www.scholastic.co.uk

The best size

Is there a best size for a parachute?

✤ Make five parachutes from squares of paper cut out to the sizes given in the table below.

✤ Test each one three times to find out which is the best.

Drop each one from the same height.

✤ Complete the table to find out the best size.

YOU WILL NEED

- 1cm squared paper;
- thread;
- scissors;
- sticky tape;
- Plasticine
- a stop-watch.

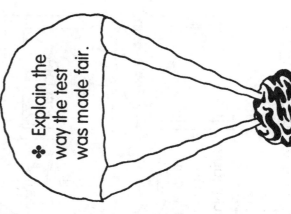

✤ Explain the way the test was made fair.

Size	Time 1	Time 2	Time 3	Average time
20cm X 20cm				
30cm X 30cm				
50cm X 50cm				
60cm X 60cm				
80cm X 80cm				

The optimum size is _____

Name _____

What can electricity do?

♣ Write the name of each item shown on this sheet into the table below. You may write some in more than once.

What can electricity do?	Things that use electricity in this way
Change into **heat**	
Change into **light**	
Change into **movement**	
Change into **sound**	
Become **magnetic**	

♣ Think of five more things that use electricity and add them to the table.

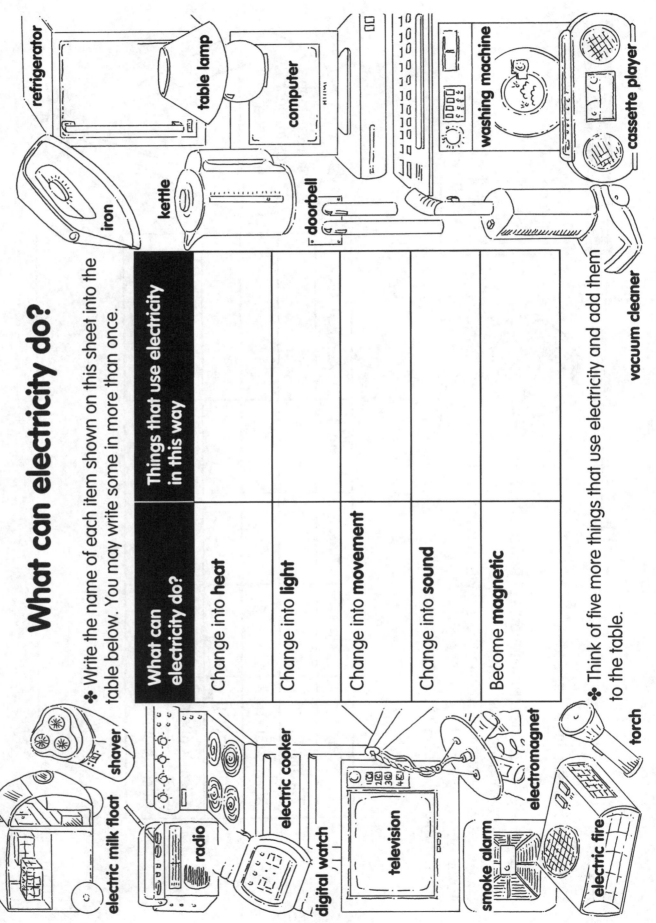

refrigerator

table lamp

computer

washing machine

cassette player

iron

kettle

doorbell

vacuum cleaner

shaver

electric milk float

radio

electric cooker

digital watch

television

smoke alarm

electromagnet

torch

electric fire

NO FUSS
PHOTOCOPIABLE

SCHOLASTIC
www.scholastic.co.uk

Name _____

Making it flow

✤ Which materials conduct electricity (that is, let it flow through them)? Carry out this investigation to find out.

You will need: a battery, a bulb in a holder, some wires with crocodile connectors.

1 Make an electrical circuit to light a bulb, as shown below.
2 Now add an extra crocodile connector wire to your circuit.

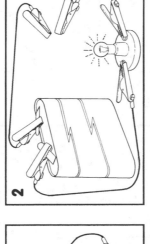

1

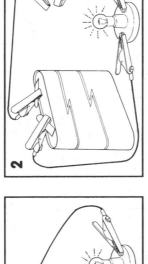

2

3 Collect some things made with different materials; for example: aluminium foil, string, polythene, an iron key, a brass screw, an elastic band, a plastic pen top, water, a coin, stainless steel, wood, a wire pipe cleaner or pencil 'lead'.

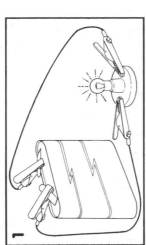

string

elastic band

wire pipe cleaner

stainless steel

plastic pen top

 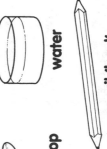 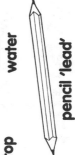

water

pencil 'lead'

4 Clip each of these things in turn between the crocodile connectors. Does the electricity still flow to the bulb?

5 Complete this table to record your results.

Object	Made of:	Conducts electricity?
foil	aluminium	

✤ What do you notice about the things that conduct electricity?

📚 **SCHOLASTIC**
www.scholastic.co.uk

NO FUSS
PHOTOCOPIABLE

Making switches

✤ Make the electrical circuit shown below.

You will need: a battery, a bulb in a holder, some wires with crocodile connectors.

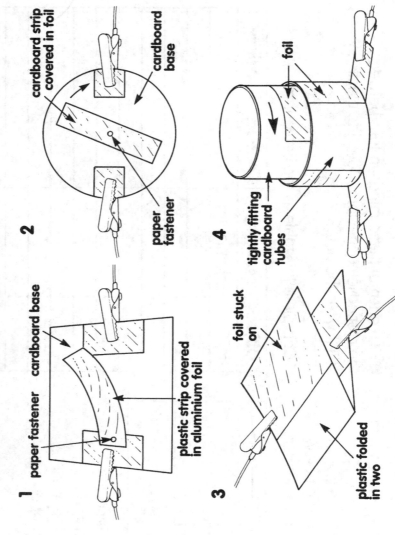

A

Join these connectors to light the bulb

✤ Now make the switches shown below.

You will need: cardboard, adhesive, aluminium foil, paper fasteners.

1 paper fastener   cardboard base

plastic strip covered in aluminium foil

2 cardboard strip covered in foil

cardboard base

paper fastener

3 foil stuck on

plastic folded in two

4 foil

tightly fitting cardboard tubes

✤ Connect your switches into the circuit at A to see if they work.

✤ Can you invent a switch of your own?

NO FUSS PHOTOCOPIABLE

■SCHOLASTIC
www.scholastic.co.uk

YOU WILL NEED
• stiff cardboard or Corriflute;
• paper clips;
• paper;
• plastic-coated wire;
• wire strippers.

2 X 2	30
3 X 3	56
5 X 6	9
7 X 6	64
9 X 7	63
8 X 8	4
7 X 8	42

A question and answer machine

✤ Make a question and answer machine as shown in the diagram below:

Back

Front

2 x 2	30
3 x 3	56
5 x 6	9
7 x 6	64
9 x 7	63
8 x 8	4
7 x 8	42

NB Always use plastic-coated wire here. Only bare the ends.

✤ Construct a simple circuit.
✤ Place one wire on a question (for example, 3 X 3) and the other on the answer.
   If you are right the bulb will light up.
♣ Can you explain how this machine works?

Given opposite is a ready-made tables sheet. Alternatively, make up one of your own.

Name _____

The respiratory system

You will need: a plastic bottle; Plasticine; a straw; a plastic top or cork and a balloon.

The respiratory system is the name given to our breathing organs. Our lungs are like large, soft sponges. Oxygen from the air we breathe in is picked up by the red blood cells in the blood in the lungs and then taken all around the body in our blood. We breathe out air containing less oxygen but more carbon dioxide and water vapour.

Activity 1
▲ Count how many times you breathe in one minute, then jog on the spot for a while. Count your breaths again. What do you notice?
▲ Use reference books to help you label the diagram below.

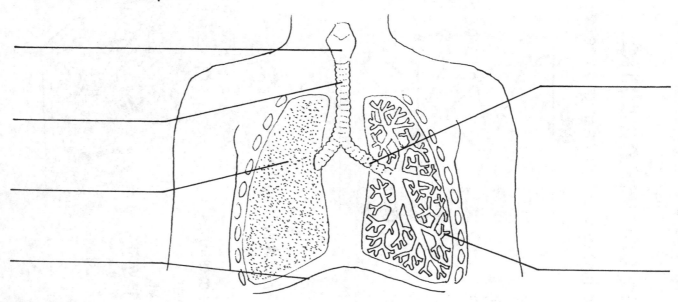

Activity 2
▲ Make a model of your lungs as in the diagram on the right then do the experiment below to find out how your lungs work. (Be sure that the Plasticine seal around the straw in the neck of the bottle is airtight.)

1 Push the balloon at the bottom of the jar. This is like your diaphragm.
2 Hold your fingers above the straw. What can you feel? What happens to the balloon inside the bottle?
3 Keep pulling out and pushing in the 'diaphragm'. Watch the balloon. It acts like your lungs.

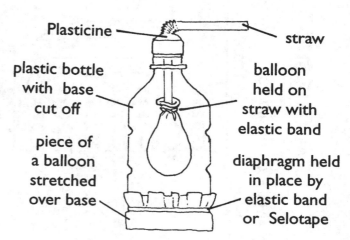

Plasticine
straw
plastic bottle with base cut off
balloon held on straw with elastic band
piece of a balloon stretched over base
diaphragm held in place by elastic band or Selotape

NO FUSS PHOTOCOPIABLE

■SCHOLASTIC
www.scholastic.co.uk

Name _____

The heart

You will need: a piece of thin card; scissors; a craft knife and cutting board.

The circulatory system consists of the heart, arteries, veins and the blood. Blood is pumped around the body by the heart. It carries food and oxygen to the muscles and organs. Arteries carry blood away from the heart and veins carry it back to the heart.

Activity 1
▲ Find pictures of the human circulatory system in reference books.
▲ Label the diagram of a heart below using the words in the box.

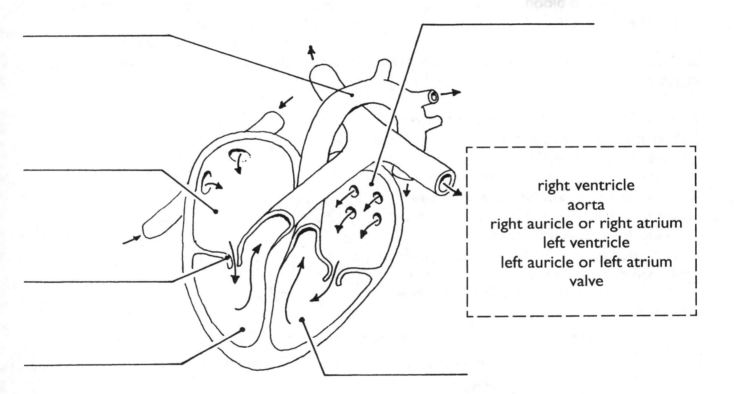

right ventricle
aorta
right auricle or right atrium
left ventricle
left auricle or left atrium
valve

Activity 2
There are special valves in the heart, veins and arteries which keep the blood flowing in one direction only.

▲ Make your own model valve.

1 Copy or trace the shape on the right on to the piece of card.
2 Cut out the shape.
3 Using a cutting board and craft knife, cut along the dotted lines. (*Be careful, cut slowly.*)
4 Push your finger into the valve from behind. What do you notice?

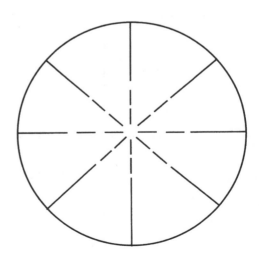

SCHOLASTIC
www.scholastic.co.uk

Heartbeat rate

You will need: a stopwatch or watch with a second hand; a chair and a playground.

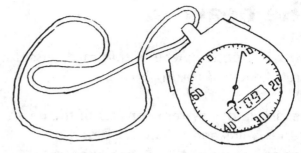

Your heart is part of the circulatory system. It is a muscular organ which pumps blood around your body in the blood vessels. Each time your heart contracts, it is called the heartbeat. As the blood rushes through an artery there is a pulse.

▲ Conduct this experiment to find out more about your heartbeat.

1 First, find your pulse. Place three fingers (not your thumb) on your wrist and count the number of beats in half a minute (then double it for one minute). Record your results.
2 Now stand still and do 20 arm swings. Count your heartbeats or pulse as soon as you stop. Record your results.
3 Ask your partner to hold a chair steady while you step up and down from the seat 40 times. Now count your pulse and record the results.

4 Finally, run around in the playground for two minutes. Again count your pulse and record the results.
▲ Ask your partner to do these tasks and record the results. Compare these results with others in your class.
▲ Why do you think your heartbeat changes? Discuss your reasons with others.

name	number of beats per minute at rest	number of beats per minute after exercise		
		20 arm swings	40 step-ups	running for two minutes

NO FUSS
PHOTOCOPIABLE

SCHOLASTIC
www.scholastic.co.uk

A balanced diet

To stay healthy, we need to eat certain types of food each day. Here are some of the things we need:

Two or three servings of:	One serving of:	Very small amounts of:
BREAD CEREAL	MILK FISH CHEESE	SUGAR OIL
VEGETABLES WATER	MEAT/POULTRY EGGS	MARGARINE/BUTTER
FRUIT	NUTS	

▲ Plan three meals for one day to be sure you have a balanced diet. Draw the food on the plates below. Can you include dessert and drinks?

▲ Keep a diary of all the food you eat in one week. Are you eating a balanced diet? Share your diary with others and compare the foods you eat.

Breakfast

Lunch   **Dinner**

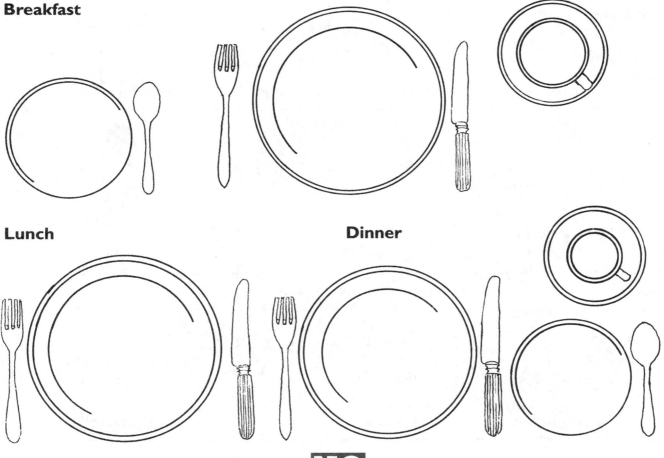

Name _____

Hygiene

It is important to keep our bodies clean to protect us from germs which may cause illness. We should wash our hands before and after certain activities to prevent us spreading or catching germs. Do you know what these activities are?

▲ Cut out the squares below.

▲ After which of the activities should you wash your hands? Sort them into groups – washing before and washing after the activity or both. Now discuss the way you have sorted the activities with others. Do they agree with your choices?

▲ Make a poster saying why hygiene is important.

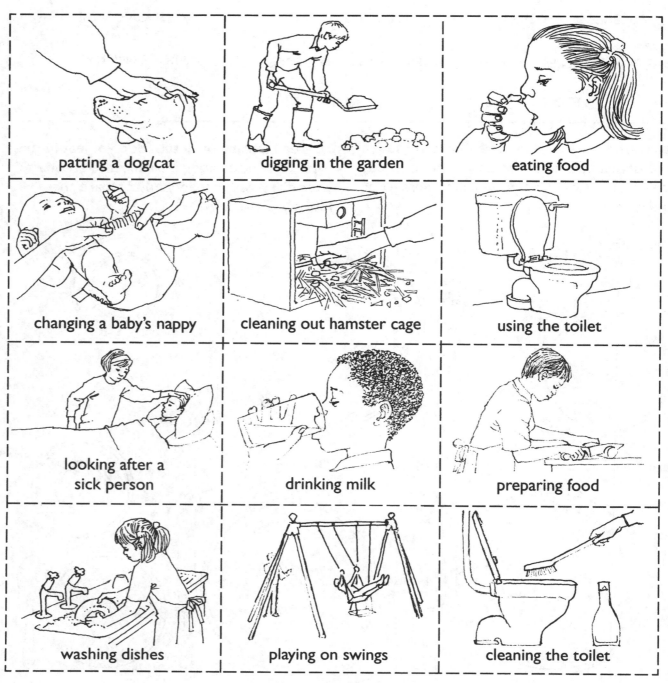

patting a dog/cat	digging in the garden	eating food
changing a baby's nappy	cleaning out hamster cage	using the toilet
looking after a sick person	drinking milk	preparing food
washing dishes	playing on swings	cleaning the toilet

SCHOLASTIC
www.scholastic.co.uk

Name _____

The life-cycle of a flowering plant

You will need: scissors; glue; card; cotton thread; colouring pencils.

▲ Make a mobile of the life-cycle of the dandelion. First colour the pictures and the word boxes. Cut along the lines. Glue each picture on to card with the matching sentence on the back. Cut out. Use cotton thread to join up the mobile in the correct order.

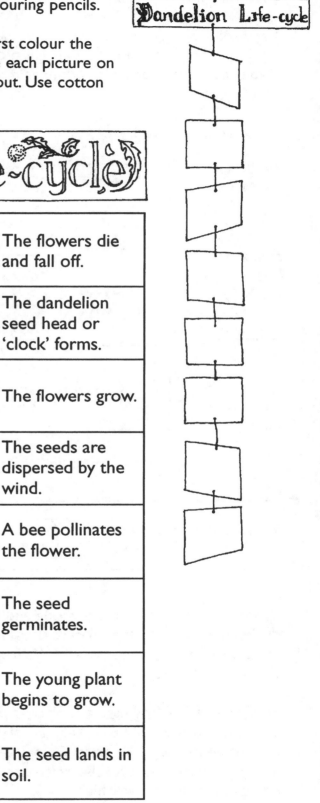

		The flowers die and fall off.
		The dandelion seed head or 'clock' forms.
		The flowers grow.
		The seeds are dispersed by the wind.
		A bee pollinates the flower.
		The seed germinates.
		The young plant begins to grow.
		The seed lands in soil.

▲ Find out about the life-cycle of another plant. Make a mobile of its life-cycle.

Animal life-cycles

You will need: a pencil; frog spawn; an ice-cream container or glass jar; reference books on frogs.

Many animals begin life as eggs inside their mother. When they are born, they are miniature versions of their parents. As they get older they grow in size but do not change the basic shape they were born with. Some animals, however, completely change their shape and form as they grow.

▲ Look at the two life-cycles below to compare how each animal develops.

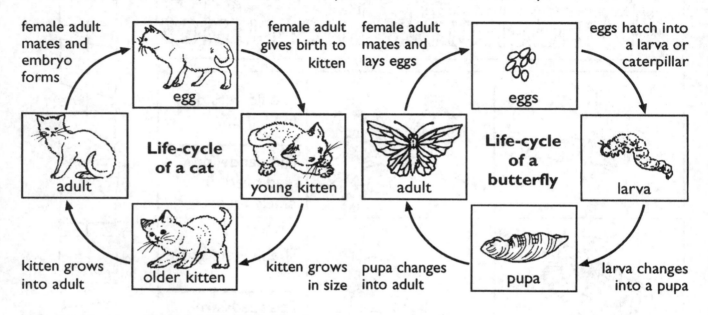

What is the same about both life-cycles?_____

_____

What is different about both life-cycles?_____

_____

When animals totally change shape and form during the life-cycle, the process is called metamorphosis. The life-cycle of the frog changes in this way.

▲ Obtain a few frog eggs and place them in a container with pond water. Keep a diary of the changes which take place. Complete the life-cycle chart opposite. Use reference books if frog spawn is not available.

▲ Find out about the life-cycles of other animals.

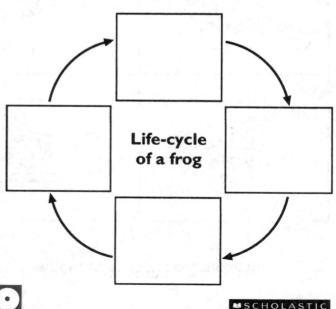

NO
FUSS
PHOTOCOPIABLE

■SCHOLASTIC
www.scholastic.co.uk

How much light do plants need?

You will need: bird seed; cotton wool; six saucers; five shoe boxes; scissors; a pencil; water.

▲ Carry out this investigation to find out how much light plants need to grow.

Place some cotton wool in each saucer and add water so that the wool is quite wet. Sprinkle bird seed on to this. Put all the saucers on a table in the sunlight. Keep one saucer uncovered but cover the other saucers with a shoe box in the following way:

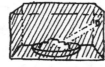

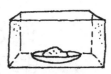

| no holes | one small hole | both ends cut out | holes cut out in bottom of all sides | turned upside down |

▲ Observe the growth of the seeds over the next few weeks. Keep the cotton wool damp. Record what happens in the table below. Discuss the results. What do they tell you?

Amount of light	What I think will happen (prediction)	What happened (result) Describe what the seedlings looked like
no cover		
no holes		
one small hole		
both ends cut out		
bottom of sides cut out		
box upside down		

▲ Find out how plants use light to help them grow. What function does the leaf have?

The parts of a flower

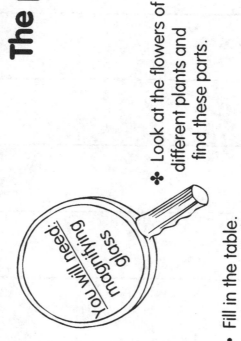

You will need: magnifying glass

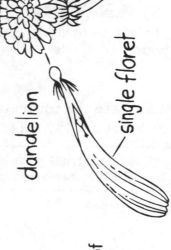

dandelion

single floret

stamen

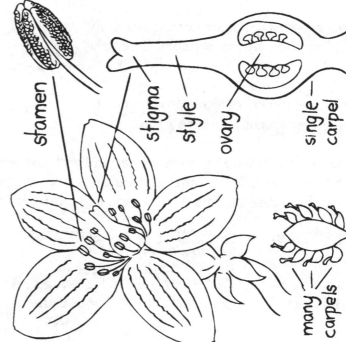

stigma

style

ovary

single carpel

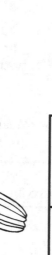

many carpels

* How many florets make a dandelion?

* Look at the flowers of different plants and find these parts.

* Fill in the table.

Name of flower	How many petals?	How many stamens?	Shape of carpel

NO FUSS PHOTOCOPIABLE

SCHOLASTIC
www.scholastic.co.uk

Pollination

Insect pollination

✿ Look out for a bee visiting flowers. Watch it for one or more minutes. How many flowers does it visit in this time?

✿ Look for these insects visiting flowers:

beetles

bumble bee

flies

honey bee

✿ Make a table with these headings:

Flower colour	Insects found

✿ Do you find more insects on one colour of flower?

✿ What else could attract them?

You will need: magnifying glass, black card

Wind pollination

✿ Collect pollen from wind pollinated flowers on black card. Look at the pollen with a magnifying glass and say what you see.

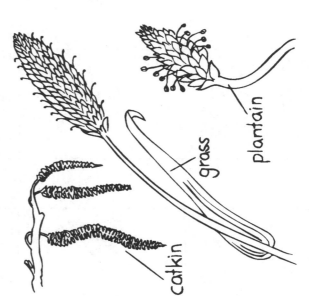

catkin

grass

plantain

Name _____

Reproduction and the human life-cycle

In order to make new humans, we need to reproduce. A human baby takes nine months to develop inside the mother's womb. The baby is attached to the womb by the umbilical cord. When the baby is born, this cord is cut and tied into a knot. This is your navel or tummy button.

▲ Can you identify the parts labelled on the diagrams of the male and female reproductive organs on the right? You may need to use reference books to help you.

▲ Now cut out the four pictures at the bottom of the page and glue them into the correct places on this diagram of the human life-cycle.

male reproductive organs

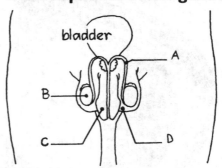

bladder

female reproductive organs

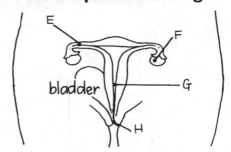

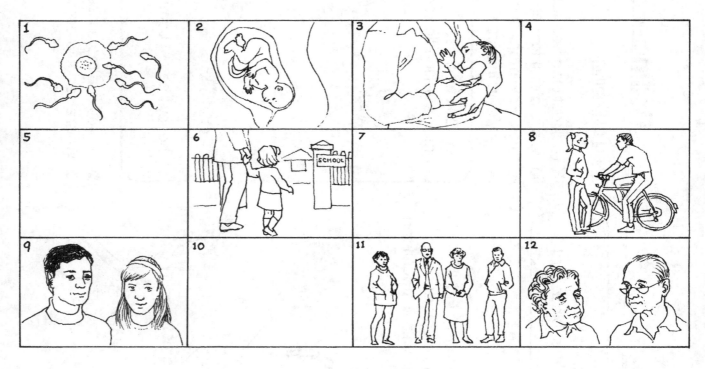

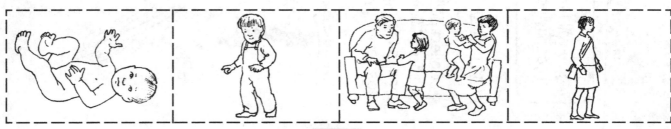

NO FUSS PHOTOCOPIABLE

■SCHOLASTIC
www.scholastic.co.uk

Name _____

Looking at gases

You will need: scissors; paper; crayons; thread.

Most gases are difficult to see. They move into spaces in all directions and are difficult to control.
▲ Look around for signs of gases.

▲ How are gases useful in each of these pictures?

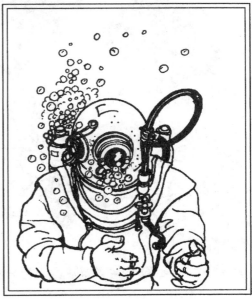

The air around us is made up of different gases:
Nitrogen   78%
Oxygen   21%
Carbon dioxide 0.03%
Other gases   0.97%

Air rises when it is warm.
▲ Make a spiral snake to hang above a radiator.
It will detect rising air.
1 Draw a spiral.
2 Colour the snake and give it an eye.
3 Cut along the line.
4 Fasten it to a piece of thread.
5 Hold it carefully over the hot radiator. What happens to the snake?

■SCHOLASTIC
www.scholastic.co.uk

NO FUSS
PHOTOCOPIABLE

Making and collecting gases

You will need: two small plastic bottles;
a balloon; bicarbonate of soda; vinegar;
a teaspoon; a paper funnel; a pencil.

When some materials are mixed together,
a gas is made.
▲ Try this experiment to make a gas.
1 Put a teaspoonful of bicarbonate of
soda into a bottle. Use a paper funnel.
2 Carefully pour a small amount of vinegar
into the bottle.
3 Put your thumb over the opening of the bottle.
▲ What do you feel? What do you see?
What do you hear?

▲ Practise fitting the balloon
over the neck of another bottle.
You will need to be able to do
this quickly.
1 Mix the bicarbonate of soda
and vinegar again.
2 Put the balloon over the neck
of the bottle as quickly as you can.
3 Describe what happens.
▲ Where did the gas go in the
first test? Where did the gas go
in the second test?

▲ Write down the names of any gases you know.

▲ Add to your collection of names as you learn more about gases.

SCHOLASTIC
www.scholastic.co.uk

Name _____

Comparing solids, liquids and gases

You will need: a pencil.

▲ Do the words below describe a solid, a liquid or a gas? Write them on the chart in the correct spaces. Some descriptions can be used more than once.

keeps its own shape
spreads out in all directions
takes the shape of the container it is in
flows down hills
flows easily through a pipe

has no definite shape
can be squashed into a smaller volume
drips
can sometimes be used for building
is usually easy to handle

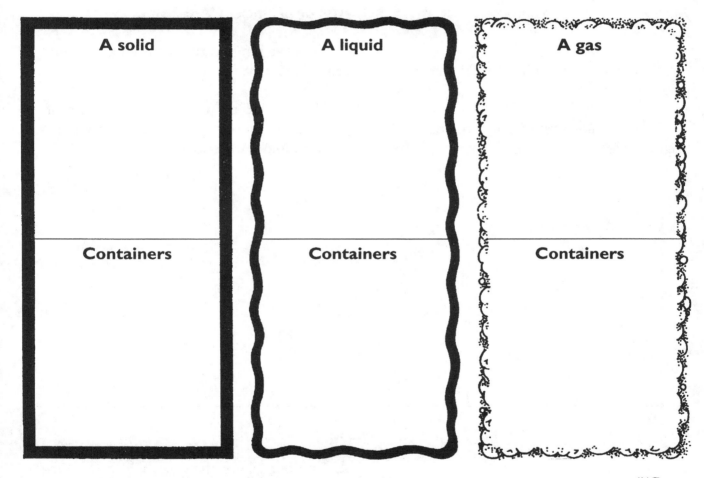

A solid	A liquid	A gas
Containers	Containers	Containers

▲ Are these containers useful for holding a solid, a liquid or a gas?

a balloon   a bottle   a straw
a schoolbag   a jar   a flask
a pair of lungs   an oxygen cylinder a box
a cupboard   a hose-pipe

▲ Add their names to the table. Some containers could be useful for holding two different materials.

www.scholastic.co.uk

How is the 'greenhouse effect' produced?

You will need: two polystyrene cups; two thermometers; soil; a small sheet of glass or perspex; coloured pens.

Scientists believe that pollution gases in the atmosphere act like the glass of a greenhouse. These gases allow energy from the Sun to reach the Earth's surface but stop heat being lost. Eventually the Earth will warm up.

▲ Conduct this experiment to see for yourself how the 'greenhouse effect' is produced.

1. Put the same amount of soil in each of the two cups.

2. One morning stand both containers in bright sunlight.

3. Take the temperature of the soil in each container. Then cover one with the sheet of glass or perspex. (CAREFUL!)

4. Take the temperature of each container every hour during the rest of the day.

5. Use two different coloured pens to plot your results on this graph. Work out a scale for the temperature axis first.

temperature

| 0 | 1 | 2 | 3 | 4 |

hours

▲ What effect does the glass have?

▲ Find out where the gases which produce the greenhouse effect come from. What can be done to stop them?

_____

_____

_____

_____

SCHOLASTIC
www.scholastic.co.uk

Name _____

The water cycle

Water is continually moving into the atmosphere by evaporation. It returns to earth in the form of snow, rain, dew and hail. On the way, water is used and changed in some way by plants and animals, including humans.

▲ Using reference books to help you, decide which word from the box describes each stage in the water cycle diagram. Some words may be used more than once.

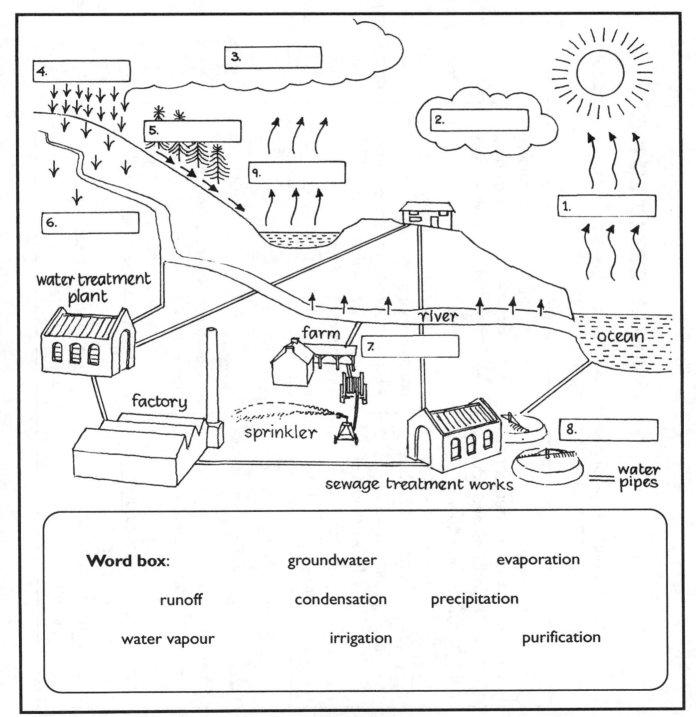

Word box:

	groundwater	evaporation
runoff	condensation	precipitation
water vapour	irrigation	purification

Name _____

Using water at school

✽ How much water is used at your school every day? Conduct this survey to find out.
♣ Discuss with your friends ways of reducing this amount.

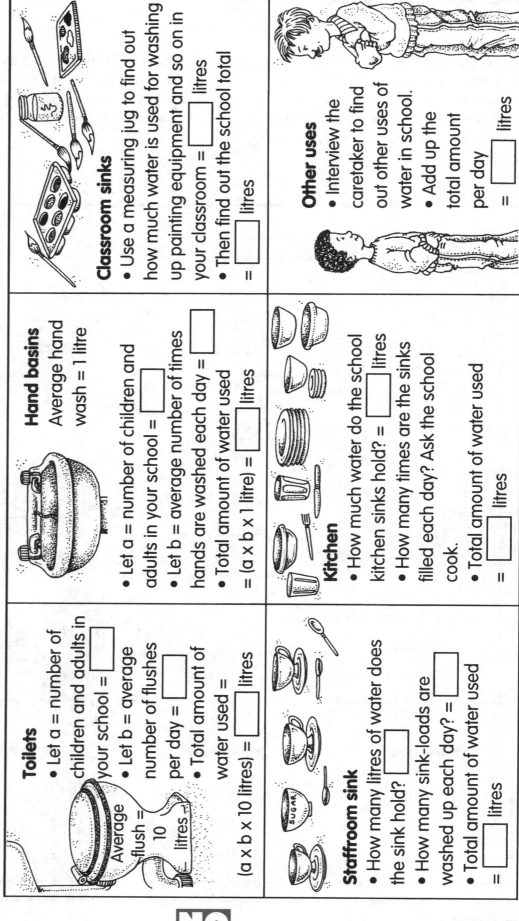

Classroom sinks
- Use a measuring jug to find out how much water is used for washing up painting equipment and so on in your classroom = ☐ litres
- Then find out the school total = ☐ litres

Other uses
- Interview the caretaker to find out other uses of water in school.
- Add up the total amount per day
= ☐ litres

Hand basins
Average hand wash = 1 litre
- Let a = number of children and adults in your school = ☐
- Let b = average number of times hands are washed each day = ☐
- Total amount of water used = (a × b × 1 litre) = ☐ litres

Kitchen
- How much water do the school kitchen sinks hold? = ☐ litres
- How many times are the sinks filled each day? Ask the school cook.
- Total amount of water used = ☐ litres

Toilets
Average flush = 10 litres
- Let a = number of children and adults in your school = ☐
- Let b = average number of flushes per day = ☐
- Total amount of water used = (a × b × 10 litres) = ☐ litres

Staffroom sink
- How many litres of water does the sink hold? = ☐
- How many sink-loads are washed up each day? = ☐
- Total amount of water used = ☐ litres

NO FUSS PHOTOCOPIABLE

SCHOLASTIC
www.scholastic.co.uk

How much water do you use?

❖ Find out how much water your family uses in one week by completing this survey. Use a calculator to help you.

❖ Compare your results with others in your class. Make suggestions as to how water can be saved at home.

Activity	Average amount of water used (litres)	Number of times each activity is carried out in one week (tally)	Weekly amount of water used (number of litres each activity uses × number of times activity is carried out in one week)
flushing toilet	10		
washing hands	1		
cleaning teeth	1		
bath	80		
shower	30		
full washing-machine load	125		
washing-up by hand	5		
washing-up by machine	65		
pot of tea	2		
car wash – bucket	25		
watering garden – watering can	25		
watering garden – hose	100		
other			
Total			

■SCHOLASTIC
www.scholastic.co.uk

Name _____

Why is it hotter in summer than in winter?

You will need: a globe; a desk lamp; a large sheet of card with a hole in the middle.

▲ Conduct this experiment to find out why it is hotter in summer than in winter. Work with a friend in a darkened room.

1. Stand the globe on a table.

2. Place the desk lamp about one metre away, switch it on and point its light at the globe. Pretend the lamp is the Sun.

3. Hold the sheet of card between the lamp and the globe so that a narrow beam of light shines on the globe.

4. Turn the globe so that the North Pole is tilting away from the lamp. This is what happens in winter.

5. Now turn the North Pole towards the lamp. This is what happens in summer.

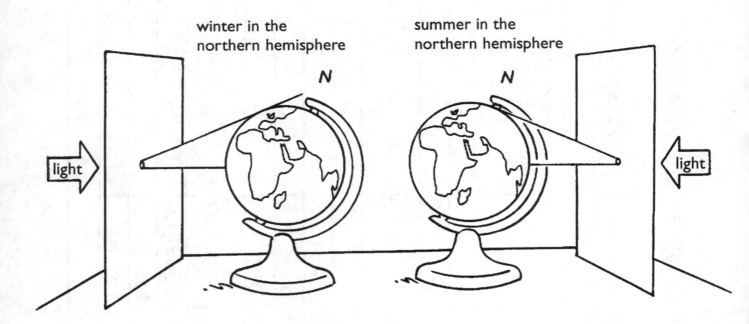

winter in the northern hemisphere

summer in the northern hemisphere

- Where is the light brightest?

- Where is the light brightest?

_____

_____

_____

_____

SCHOLASTIC
www.scholastic.co.uk

Name _____

Seasonal changes

You will need: a pencil.

Animals and plants change with the seasons.

▲ Write or draw what these animals and plants do in summer and winter. One has been started for you.

	Spring	Summer	Autumn	Winter
Deciduous trees	Leaf buds burst.	Lots of leaves.		
Evergreen trees				
Flowers				
Fruits				
Hedgehogs				
Bats				
Frogs				
Swallows				
Robins				

www.scholastic.co.uk

YOU WILL NEED
- a piece of dowelling;
- a cork;
- a cotton reel;
- a large piece of cardboard;
- adhesive;
- pencils.

Build a sundial

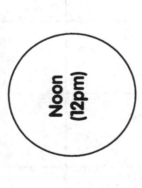

Noon (12pm)

A cork to protect the end

A piece of dowelling

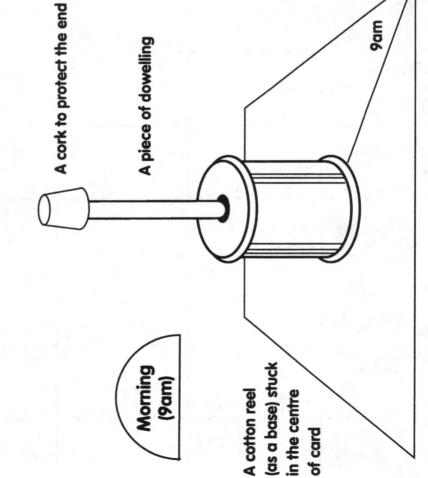

9am

A cotton reel (as a base) stuck in the centre of card

Morning (9am)

Evening (3pm)

❖ Follow this diagram to make a sundial. Try it out on a sunny day.

❖ Place the sundial outside in a safe place.

❖ Draw the shadow of the dowel at 9am and at each hour until home-time.

❖ What happens to the position of the shadow during the day?

NO FUSS PHOTOCOPIABLE

■ SCHOLASTIC
www.scholastic.co.uk

Earth and Moon dance

✤ Devise a dance or movement with a friend to explain the way in which the Earth orbits the Sun and the Moon orbits the Earth. Use the picture below to help you.

YOU WILL NEED
- a small table;
- a lamp;
- a large ball (Earth);
- a smaller ball (Moon).

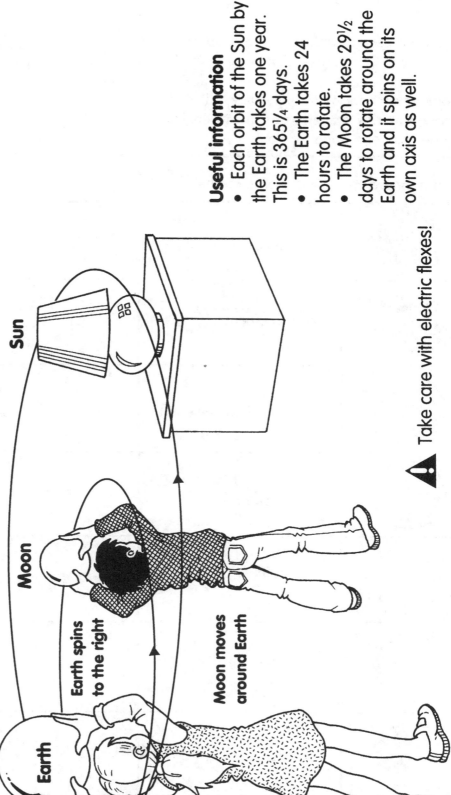

Earth moves around the Sun and spins

Sun

Moon

Earth spins to the right

Moon moves around Earth

Earth

Useful information
- Each orbit of the Sun by the Earth takes one year. This is 365¼ days.
- The Earth takes 24 hours to rotate.
- The Moon takes 29½ days to rotate around the Earth and it spins on its own axis as well.

⚠ Take care with electric flexes!

Changes in the moon

Throughout each month the moon appears to change shape. Can you suggest why?

▲ Look at each moon shape. Draw a diagram to show how this shape has been caused. The first one has been done for you.

▲ Try to watch the moon changes at night from where you live. Record the changing shapes.

Moon phase	Name of phase	Why it looks like this
	new	sun ⟶ E
	crescent	
	first quarter (half)	
	gibbous	
	full	
	gibbous	
	last quarter	
	crescent	

NO FUSS
PHOTOCOPIABLE

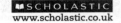

SCHOLASTIC
www.scholastic.co.uk

Solids and shadows

We can only see things if they give out light or if they reflect light from somewhere else.

✤ Investigate light and shadow patterns on solid shapes.
• Find some three-dimensional shapes, like these:

• Put the shapes in a darkened place and shine a torch on them from the side.

• On the back of this sheet, draw the parts of each shape which are in the light.

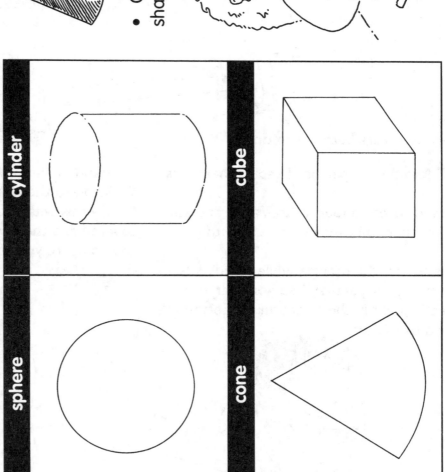

cylinder

sphere

cube

cone

SCHOLASTIC
www.scholastic.co.uk

NO FUSS
PHOTOCOPIABLE

Name _____

The senses: hearing

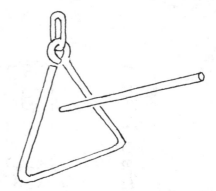

You will need: a blindfold; a small musical triangle and a trundle wheel.

▲ How far away can you hear a sound? Try these activities to find out.

Activity 1

1 Blindfold your partner (be sure to keep their ears free).
2 Stand one metre behind your partner and softly strike the triangle. Can your partner hear it?

3 Now step back another metre and try again. Keep trying until your partner cannot hear and make a chart to record the results.
4 Try this indoors and outdoors. Is there a different result? Can you suggest why?

Activity 2
▲ Are two ears better than one?

1 Blindfold your partner, keeping their ears free.
2 Stand three to four metres away and ask your partner to cover up one ear with their hand.
3 Gently hit the triangle while standing to the left of your partner. Can your partner correctly point in the direction of the sound? Record the result.

4 Stand in line with your partner. Repeat.
5 Stand to the right of your partner. Repeat.
6 Try this with your partner's other ear covered and then with both ears free. Record and compare your results.

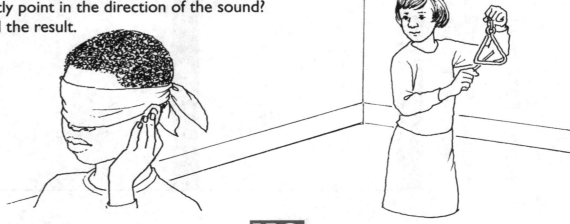

NO FUSS PHOTOCOPIABLE

■ SCHOLASTIC
www.scholastic.co.uk

Sound survey

♣ Make a sound survey at different places around school.
Listen very, very carefully. Close your eyes if you want. Then fill in this table.

Time of day	Where I listened	What made the sound?	How far away (close/middle/far)?	Single sound or continuous?	It sounds like …

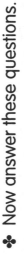

✱ Now answer these questions.

- Where did you hear the greatest number of different sounds?
- Which was the loudest sound you heard?
- Which was the quietest sound you heard?
- Does the time of day make a difference to your results?

Name _____

What makes sounds?

Your voice makes sounds.

* Hum a tune quietly.

* Feel your neck.

* Does your neck feel the same when you whisper something?

An elastic band makes sounds.

* Ping the elastic band.

* Watch the elastic band closely.

* On the back of this sheet, draw a picture of the elastic band when it is making a sound.

A ruler can make sounds.

* Ping the ruler.

* Listen and watch the ruler closely.

* On the back of this sheet, draw the ruler when it is making a sound.

A chime bar can make sounds.

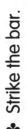
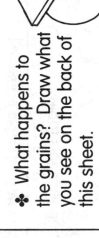

* Sprinkle salt or sand on the chime bar.

* Strike the bar.

* What happens to the grains? Draw what you see on the back of this sheet.

NO FUSS
PHOTOCOPIABLE

SCHOLASTIC
www.scholastic.co.uk

Name _____

High and low sounds

The highness or lowness of a sound is called its **pitch**.
✤ Quietly hum a low pitched sound and then a high pitched sound.
✤ Find out which of these things make a low pitched sound and which a high pitched sound.
✤ For each of these activities, draw each item in the correct column on the table to show whether it makes a low, medium or high pitched sound.

Sounds made by...	Pitch		
	Low	**Medium**	**High**
Three jars with different amounts of water. Tap each in turn with a pencil.			
Ping the elastic band, then move the support outwards and ping again.			
Blow across an empty lemonade bottle. Then try with different amounts of water.			
Ping a ruler at different places on the edge of a table.			

✤ Circle the correct word in this sentence:
High pitched sounds are made when the size of the vibrating thing is small/medium/large.

* Write down how an earthworm moves (or tell a teacher or a friend).

Record here:

⚠ Wash your hands after you have handled the earthworm.

How earthworms move

You will need:
large earthworm
paper towel
magnifying glass

♣ Carefully put the earthworm on a paper towel.

♣ Watch the earthworm move. What shape is its head end? What shape is its tail end?

♣ Put your ear close to the moving earthworm. What can you hear?

♣ Turn the earthworm over. *Gently* rub a finger along its skin. What can you feel?

♣ Look at the earthworm with a magnifying glass. What can you see?

NO FUSS
PHOTOCOPIABLE

■SCHOLASTIC
www.scholastic.co.uk

Investigating birds' beaks

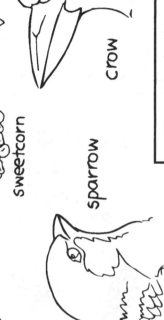

pigeon

crow

mallard

sparrow

millet   biscuit

sweetcorn

Beak	Pieces picked up per minute		
	millet	corn	biscuit
tweezers			
chopsticks			
tongs			
servers			

You will need:
stopclock, beak models and foods
shown on this page, My planning
sheets 1 and 2, My results sheet,
Looking at my results sheet

✿ How does the size of a bird's beak
affect the size of food it can pick up?
✿ Use these model beaks to find out.

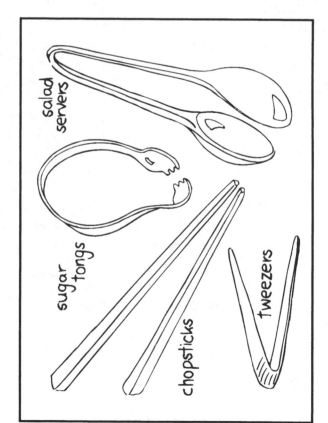

salad servers

sugar tongs

chopsticks

tweezers

Name _____

Seed dispersal

You will need: a pencil.

Many seeds are made in a special way to help them travel a long way when they are dispersed. This allows plants of the same type to grow in new areas and not become too crowded in one place.

▲ Seeds can be dispersed in many different ways. Below are some examples. Look at the shapes of the seeds. Write down your ideas about how the design of the seed might help it to be dispersed in the way it is.

Type of dispersal	Seed example	How I think the seed design helps it to be dispersed
Wind The wind blows the seed away from the parent plant.	dandelion	
Animal **a** Birds eat the fruit and the seeds pass out in their droppings. **b** The seeds catch in the fur of animals.	**a** blackberry **b** burdock	
Explosion The seeds have an outer pod which splits and pushes the seeds out.	lupin	
Water The seed floats away in the water of ponds, rivers or oceans.	coconut	

▲ Now look at these seeds. Decide how they might be dispersed – wind, animal, explosion or water. Write your answer underneath each picture. Do others agree with your choices?

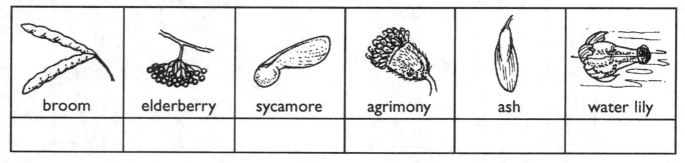

broom	elderberry	sycamore	agrimony	ash	water lily

▲ Make some model seeds that could be dispersed by the wind. Test them to see which one works best. Why?

SCHOLASTIC
www.scholastic.co.uk

Name _____

Food chains

You will need: a pencil.

Living things can be either producers or consumers. Green plants are *producers*. They are able to manufacture their own food using a process called photosynthesis. *Consumers* are living things which eat other living things.

▲ Look at the plants and animals below. Decide if each is a producer (P) or consumer (C). Write the letter P or C in the box for each one.

grass ☐	hedgehog ☐	shrub ☐	rabbit ☐	roe deer ☐	wheat ☐
	eats slugs, worms and insects		eats grass	eats grass	
flowering plant ☐	vole ☐	slug ☐	tawny owl ☐	human ☐	fox ☐
	eats grass and wheat	eats leaves	eats mice and voles	eats plants and animals	eats rabbits, mice and voles

Food chains show the feeding relationships between living things. Nearly all food chains begin with a green plant or producer. The plant is eaten by an animal, which in turn is eaten by another animal and so on.

▲ Use the plants and animals above to write down some food chains. Here is one example for you:

grass ———► rabbit ———► fox

▲ Find out what other animals eat and make some more food chains.

www.scholastic.co.uk

Name _____

Plant adaptations

You will need: a pencil.

Plants have special features which help them to survive in a particular habitat.

▲ Look at the two plants described below. Decide which features you think would help the plant to grow well in its habitat. Write these features underneath each picture. Share your ideas with others. Do they agree?

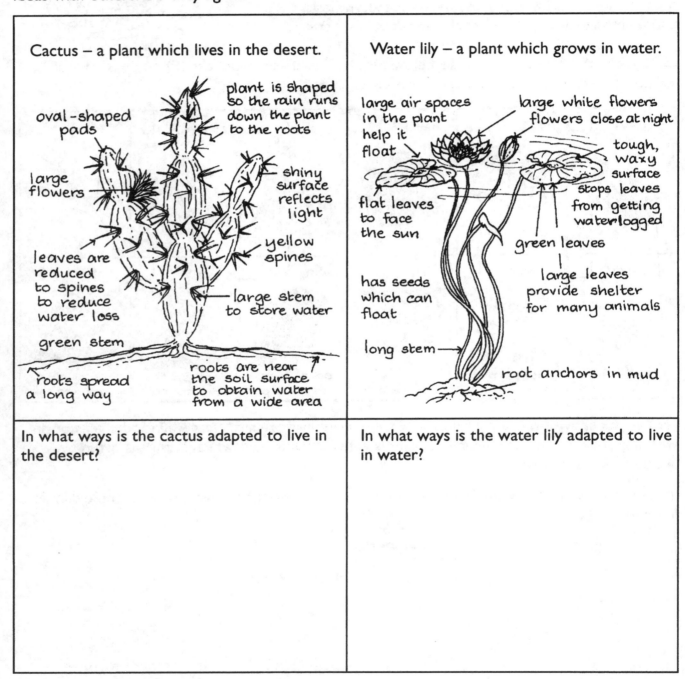

Cactus – a plant which lives in the desert.

oval-shaped pads

plant is shaped so the rain runs down the plant to the roots

large flowers

shiny surface reflects light

leaves are reduced to spines to reduce water loss

yellow spines

large stem to store water

green stem

roots spread a long way

roots are near the soil surface to obtain water from a wide area

Water lily – a plant which grows in water.

large air spaces in the plant help it float

large white flowers flowers close at night

tough, waxy surface stops leaves from getting waterlogged

flat leaves to face the sun

green leaves

has seeds which can float

large leaves provide shelter for many animals

long stem

root anchors in mud

In what ways is the cactus adapted to live in the desert?

In what ways is the water lily adapted to live in water?

▲ Find out how some plants are adapted to living on very cold mountains or in very humid places like rainforests.

NO FUSS PHOTOCOPIABLE

■ SCHOLASTIC
www.scholastic.co.uk

Name _____

Roots

You will need: a small pot plant (such as a spider plant); a jar; water; a plantlet from the spider plant; a saucer; a small piece of cotton cloth; a newspaper; a pencil.

▲ Carefully remove the pot plant from its container. Gently remove the soil from the roots (use newspaper to collect the soil). Look closely at the roots.

What colour are they? _____

Describe what they look like. _____

_____

Can you suggest why a plant has roots? _____

_____

▲ How do roots soak up water? Do this simple experiment to show capillary action:

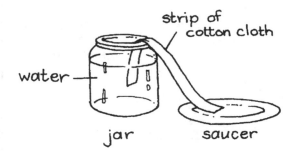

What do you think will happen?

_____

Leave for several hours. Observe what happens. Discuss what is happening.

▲ Now observe some roots growing. Place a plantlet from a spider plant in a jar of water. Observe what happens over the next few weeks. Record the results here:

Day	Description – what happens?
5	
10	
15	
20	
25	
30	
35	

▲ Grow roots in other ways, for example:
1 cuttings in water
2 growing seeds.
Compare the roots which grow.

Name _____

Using the Earth's materials

You will need: a red, orange (amber) and green crayon; a pencil.

▲ How do you think we should use the Earth's materials? Think carefully about each material in the table.
▲ Use the code to show how you think they should be used by choosing red, amber or green.
▲ Write down your suggestions and comments.

Colour Code

red — Avoid using this material. Supplies are likely to run out soon.

amber — Use this material carefully and recycle whenever possible.

green — Although supplies seem fairly plentiful, use wisely and recycle whenever possible.

Material	Supply	Red, amber or green?	Suggestions and comments
plastic	Plastic is made from oil which will eventually run out.	◯	
metal	Metals come from under the ground. Supplies are becoming low.	◯	
hardwood	Slow-growing trees produce hardwoods. Rainforest trees are hardwood.	◯	
softwood	Coniferous trees produce softwoods. They grow fairly quickly.	◯	
natural fabrics	Some animals and plants produce natural fibres for making fabrics.	◯	
paper	Paper is made from softwood trees.	◯	
glass	A special type of sand is used for making glass.	◯	

NO FUSS PHOTOCOPIABLE

SCHOLASTIC
www.scholastic.co.uk

Renewable and non-renewable resources

Non-renewable resources, once formed, do not replace themselves (except over a very, very long period of time).
Renewable resources can be replaced.

♣ Decide whether the resources named below are **non-renewable** or **renewable** and write each one under the correct heading.

Non-renewable resources	Renewable resources

♣ On the back of this sheet, suggest ways of saving the non-renewable resources you have listed.

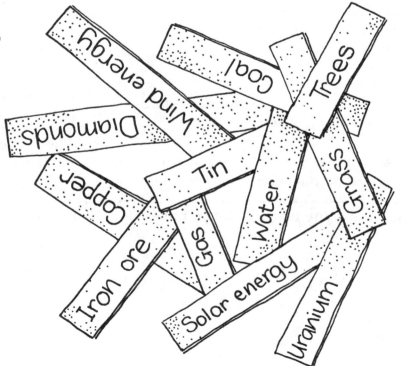

■■SCHOLASTIC
www.scholastic.co.uk

NO FUSS
PHOTOCOPIABLE

Name _____

Will it rot?

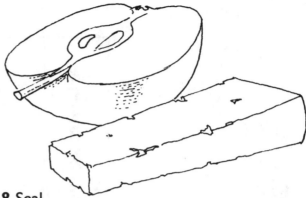

You will need: plastic food bags with ties; cheddar cheese; apples; cotton wool; water; hand lenses.

▲ Find out what happens to food kept in different conditions by doing this experiment.

1 Place a piece of cheese into three different bags.
2 Seal.
3 Place one bag in the fridge (a), one in a warm spot (b) (near a heater, sunny window ledge) and one in the room away from the sun (c).

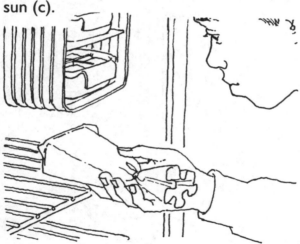

4 Do the same with pieces of apple.
5 Soak some cotton wool in water then place this in a bag with some cheese.
6 Seal.
7 In another bag, place some cheese which has been rubbed on the floor.

8 Seal.
9 Place both bags in position C.
10 Do the same with the apple.
11 Predict what might happen in each case.
▲ Record the results. Make daily observations. Note changes in colour, shape and texture.

▲ Does anything grow on the food? What is it?

Note: When observing, do not open the bags. Use a hand lens to look closely through the plastic bag.

▲ Write down the things which you think help food to rot. How can it be prevented?

SCHOLASTIC
www.scholastic.co.uk

Making compost

You will need: plastic rubbish bin with a lid; soil; grass clippings; leaves (not evergreen); vegetable and fruit waste; garden fork.

We can change food waste, which we would normally throw away, into something useful: we can make it into compost.

▲ Try making compost yourself.
1 Make holes in the bin and lid.
2 Layer the bin as follows: grass clippings and soil, vegetable/fruit waste, rotting leaves, soil... repeating until the bin is full.

3 Put on the lid and keep the bin in a sunny spot where air can get in from the sides.
4 Mix the layers regularly with a garden fork.
▲ Observe the compost every few days. Record what happens.

▲ Try out the compost when it is ready (it will be dark and crumbly). Plant two bean seeds. Use compost on one and garden soil or sand with the other. Record the results. Which bean grows best?

repeat layers

soil
rotting leaves
vegetable/fruit waste
grass clippings and soil

www.scholastic.co.uk

NO FUSS
PHOTOCOPIABLE

Name _____

Micro-organisms

You will need: a pencil.

Bacteria are microscopic living things. Some bacteria are decomposers which help to get rid of wastes. Other bacteria can cause diseases. We need to look after the food we eat to prevent bacteria making us ill.

▲ Look at each example below. Write down how you think each activity helps to kill bacteria. Share your ideas with others. Do they agree?

1 Washing hands before handling food.

2 Putting food in a refrigerator.

3 Cooking food.

4 Bottling and canning food.

▲ Make a poster telling others how to look after and store food correctly.

SCHOLASTIC
www.scholastic.co.uk

Name _____

Food care and storage

Preserved food I eat

Frozen food		
Canned food		
Bottled food		

♣ Make a large copy of this table and look for these food additives on packets and cans in your kitchen. Put a tick in the appropriate box when you find the words on the label.

Food								
Additive	Colouring	Preservative	Antioxidant	Emulsifier	Stabiliser	Sugar	Salt	Flavouring

Preparing a meal

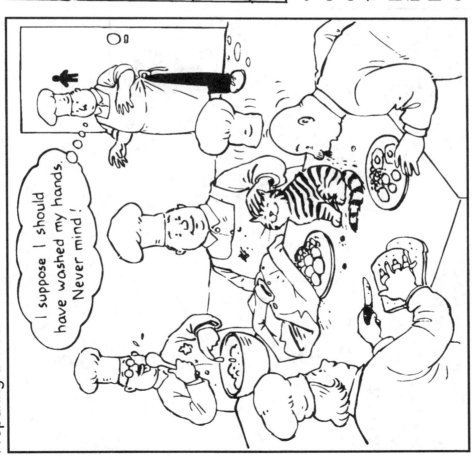

I suppose I should have washed my hands. Never mind!

♣ Where is the food being infected with germs? Mark the places with a big red cross.

■ SCHOLASTIC
www.scholastic.co.uk

NO FUSS PHOTOCOPIABLE

You will need:
scissors, glue

Bacteria cause boils, tetanus and scarlet fever. Viruses cause colds, flu, chicken pox and measles.

When you sneeze the droplets leave your nose at nearly 100 miles per hour (160kph).

Inside the body a bacterium can breed every twenty minutes like this:

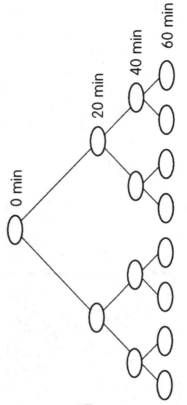

0 min
20 min
40 min
60 min

♣ Write down how many bacteria there would be after 80 minutes, 100 minutes, 200 minutes, 600 minutes.

Microbes and disease

♣ Cut out these segments and arrange them into a cycle of illness and health.
♣ Where are you in the cycle? Colour in the segment red.

Bodily defences kill microbes

Symptoms develop

Infection occurs

Full illness develops

Healthy

Almost well again

NO FUSS PHOTOCOPIABLE

SCHOLASTIC
www.scholastic.co.uk

Name _____

Separating substances

You will need: salt; water; glass; spoon; saucepan; hotplate.

Some things are made from two or more substances. Sometimes it is necessary to separate them in order to obtain one of the substances. We can do this by evaporation and filtering.

▲ Try this for yourself.
⚠ Adult supervision is needed.

1 Mix several teaspoons of salt in a glass of water until the salt dissolves.

2 Pour the solution into a saucepan and boil the water.

3 Observe what happens to the water. Where does it go? What is left over after the water has gone?

▲ Filtering
1 Set up a filter as in the diagram.
2 Fill the top with muddy water.
3 Watch the water which comes out. How has it changed?

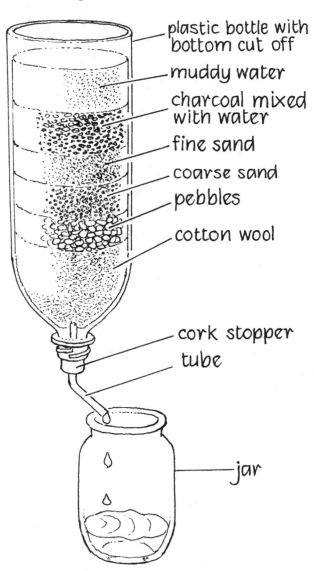

- plastic bottle with bottom cut off
- muddy water
- charcoal mixed with water
- fine sand
- coarse sand
- pebbles
- cotton wool
- cork stopper
- tube
- jar

▲ Try out simpler filters such as paper, tights, socks, fabric. Which filter works best?

Chromatography

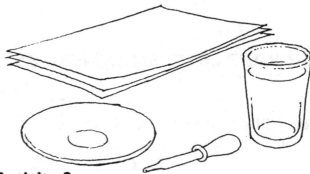

You will need: water-based felt-tipped pens; water; jars; blotting paper; food colouring; eye dropper; saucer.

Colours can be changed by mixing with other colours. Chromatography is a method used to separate all the colours which have been mixed together to make one colour.

Activity 1

1 Cut out a square of blotting paper (10cm x 10cm).
2 Draw a circle of any colour felt-tipped pen (or food colouring).
3 Place the paper over a saucer.
4 With an eye dropper, put one drop of water in the centre of the coloured dot.

Activity 2

1 Cut out strips of blotting paper (33cm x 12 cm).
2 Place a dot of colour about 2cm from one end.

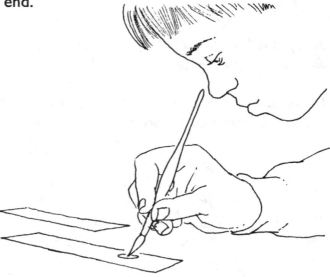

3 Put the strips into a jar of water so the dot of colour is just above the water line.
4 Watch what happens.
▲ Which colour uses the most mixtures?

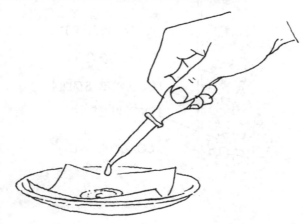

5 Wait until the ink stops spreading. Add another drop.
6 Repeat.
▲ What happens?

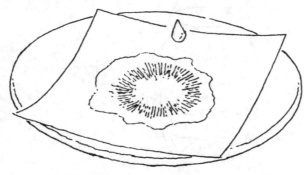

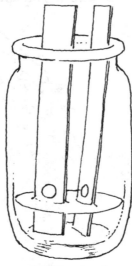

▲ Try out other colours and compare the results.

▲ Try out several different brands of the same colour, say, black. Do they all use the same colours to make black?

NO FUSS PHOTOCOPIABLE

SCHOLASTIC
www.scholastic.co.uk

Soil drainage

You will need: two empty plastic lemonade bottles, both the same size; filter paper or paper towels; clear glass jars; clay soil; sandy soil and scissors.

▲ Do this experiment to investigate the effects of water on soil.

1 Cut the two plastic bottles in half then turn the tops upside down to make two funnels.

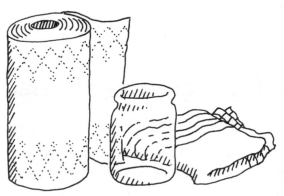

3 Now pour equal amounts of water into each funnel.

2 Place filter paper or a paper towel in the funnels then put clay soil in one funnel and sandy soil in the other.

▲ Which soil drains the quickest?

_____

_____

_____

▲ Which soil lets most water through?

_____

_____

_____

▲ Which soil would it be easiest to walk on after heavy rain?

_____

▲ In which soil would plants grow best in dry weather? Why?

_____

_____

_____

_____

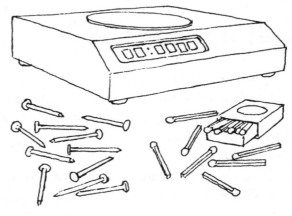

Making chemical changes

You will need: steel wool; saucer; water; nails; matches; saucer; paper; electronic scales.

Activity 1
▲ Soak some of the steel wool in water then place it on a saucer. Leave for several hours or overnight.

▲ What has happened to the steel wool? Can you suggest why this has happened?
▲ Compare this wool to the wool not placed in the water. Which is strongest?
▲ Try the same experiment with a nail. Think of ways to prevent the nail from rusting. Try out your ideas. Record the results.

Activity 2
▲ Place a lighted match in a saucer and watch it burn. When cool, touch the match.
▲ What has happened to it? How has it changed?

▲ Cut a small piece of paper and place this into the saucer. Light it with a match. Watch what happens. How has it changed?

▲ Repeat these two experiments but weigh each object before and after. What do you notice?

NO FUSS PHOTOCOPIABLE

■ SCHOLASTIC
www.scholastic.co.uk

Name _____

Manufactured changes

Humans are able to take a raw material found in nature, such as wood, and change it into something completely different. Wood can be manufactured into paper.

▲ Below is a group of things. For each object decide if it is a raw material or whether it has been changed (manufactured) in some way. Write your answer underneath each picture. You may need to discuss your ideas with a friend or use reference books to help you.

glass	diamond	oil	steel	iron ore
gold	plastic	wool	flour	aluminium
coal	salt	milk	petrol	silk

Name _____

Changes in strength

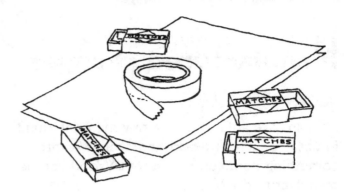

You will need: paper or thin card (A4 size); 4 matchboxes or blocks; measuring weights (1g – 1kg); sticky tape.

We can sometimes change the strength of something by altering its shape.

▲ Conduct this experiment to find out how the strength of paper can be changed.

▲ Use the paper in the following ways. See how much weight the paper will hold each time.

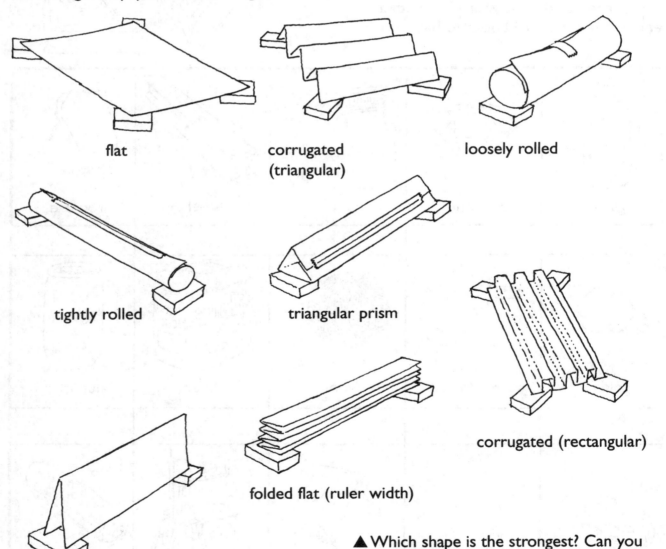

flat

corrugated (triangular)

loosely rolled

tightly rolled

triangular prism

corrugated (rectangular)

folded flat (ruler width)

folded in half

▲ Which shape is the strongest? Can you suggest why?
▲ Try out other shapes of your own. Record the results.
▲ How would these shapes affect how buildings or bridges are made?

SCHOLASTIC
www.scholastic.co.uk

Name_____

Forces at work

You will need: a pencil.

A force is a push, a pull or a twist.
A force is always needed to move something.

▲ Look at these pictures. What is moving?
Is a push, a pull or a twist moving it?
Or is it more than one of these forces?

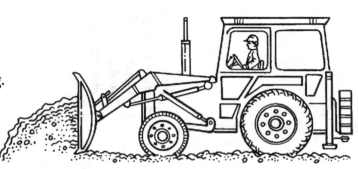

▲ Which of the pictures
shows the biggest force?

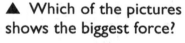

▲ Draw things you push, pull or twist every
day. Make a table like this:

object	push	pull	twist
comb		x	

www.scholastic.co.uk

Measuring forces

✿ Make this simple **force meter**.

You will need: thick card, string, a ruler, an elastic band.

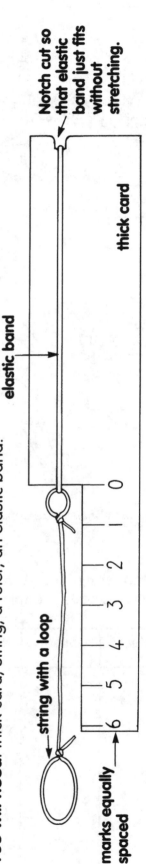

- Notch cut so that elastic band just fits without stretching.
- elastic band
- thick card
- string with a loop
- marks equally spaced

Your force meter will measure pulling forces. This car is being pulled along with a force of 3.

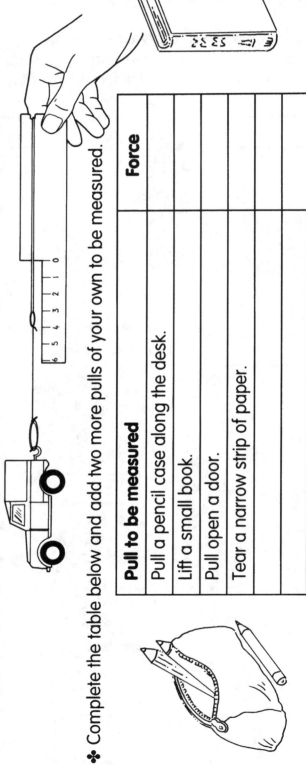

✿ Complete the table below and add two more pulls of your own to be measured.

Pull to be measured	Force
Pull a pencil case along the desk.	
Lift a small book.	
Pull open a door.	
Tear a narrow strip of paper.	

NO FUSS
PHOTOCOPIABLE

■ SCHOLASTIC
www.scholastic.co.uk

Name _____

Force meters

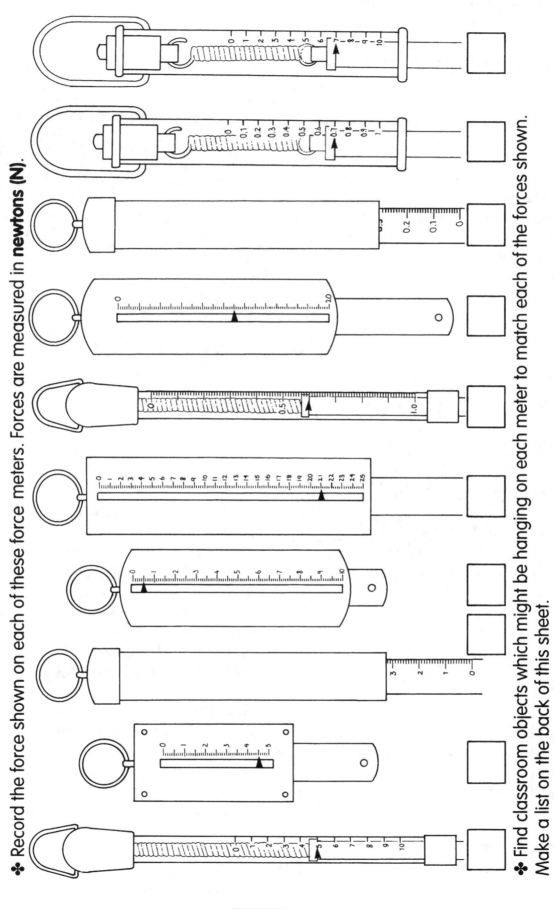

* Record the force shown on each of these force meters. Forces are measured in **newtons (N)**.

* Find classroom objects which might be hanging on each meter to match each of the forces shown. Make a list on the back of this sheet.

Name _____

Investigating gravity

You will need: Plasticine; a tape measure; a chair to stand on.

▲ Conduct this experiment. Ask a friend to help you.

1. Make four balls with the Plasticine. Make sure that they are all the same size.
2. Drop one of the balls to the floor from a height of 50 centimetres (ask your friend to measure with a tape measure).

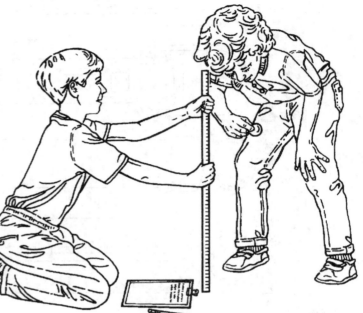

3. Carefully pick up the ball and put it on a piece of paper marked number 1.
4. Drop the second ball from a height of 1 metre. Call this number 2.
5. Drop the other two balls from 150 centimetres (number 3) and 2 metres (number 4).
6. Examine all four balls carefully. Can you see any difference between them?

▲ Describe what has happened to each of the balls. Can you explain what you see?

_____

_____

_____

_____

NO FUSS
PHOTOCOPIABLE

■SCHOLASTIC
www.scholastic.co.uk

Name _____

Bending light

We see things clearly when light is reflected off them straight into our eyes. If the reflected light is made to turn corners, then things seem to change shape.

♣ Investigate these changing shapes using a plastic drink bottle filled with water.

- Make a simple shape to look at, such as this:

- Look at the shape through the bottle.

- Record all the different images which you see through the bottle. (The shape may turn round!)

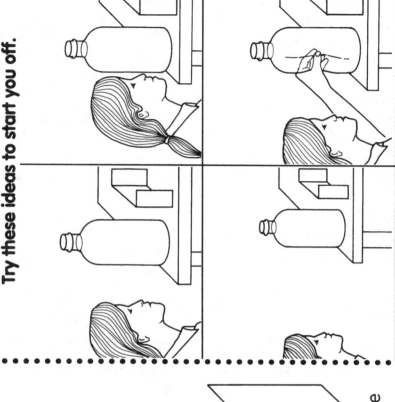

Try these ideas to start you off.

Can you make this shape appear?

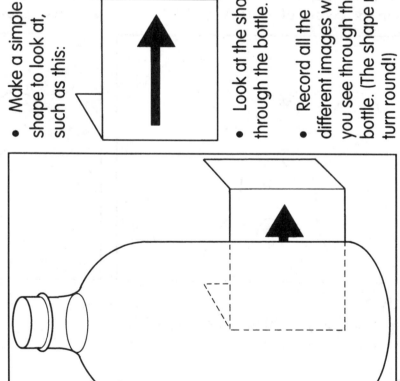

NO FUSS
PHOTOCOPIABLE

Name _____

The senses: sight

You will need: red and blue coloured pencils; scissors, coloured Cellophane (red, blue, etc.) and a ruler.

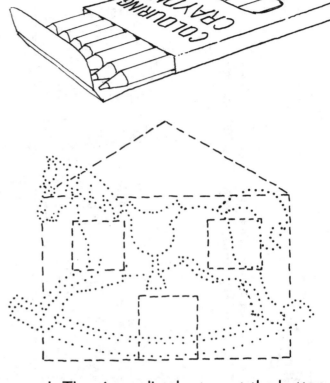

▲ Our eyes sometimes deceive us.
Try out these activities to find out how.

Activity 1
1 Colour the dotted lines in the picture opposite in blue.
2 Colour the dashed lines in red.
3 Now cut out some red Cellophane and look at the picture through the Cellophane.
▲ What happens?
▲ Try using other colours.
▲ Do some drawings of your own.

Activity 2
1 Carefully colour in the area around the figure in picture A in red.
2 Now concentrate your vision on the button in the centre of figure A for 12 seconds. Then immediately stare at the button in figure B.
▲ Now what can you see? Can you find out why this happens?

Activity 3
▲ Which line do you think is the longest? Measure them to find out.

NO FUSS
PHOTOCOPIABLE

SCHOLASTIC
www.scholastic.co.uk

See-through or not see-through

♣ Collect as many materials together as you can.

♣ Hold each up to the window.

♣ According to what you can see, stick a tiny sample of the material into the correct oval below.

YOU WILL NEED
• a large selection of wrapping materials including plastic;
• scissors;
• adhesive.

Translucent

Translucent materials let some light through.

Opaque

Opaque materials are not see-through.

Transparent

Transparent materials let light through. They are see-through.

♣ Which materials are most likely to create a shadow? _____

Reflections

You will need: a small rectangle of perspex or glass
to act as a mirror.

✤ Stand the 'mirror' along the line in each box below.
✤ Look at the reflection of each shape.
✤ What shape do you see? Draw it behind the mirror.
✤ Make up some more shapes of your own.

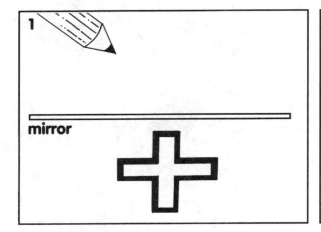

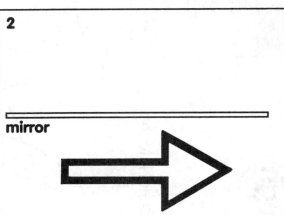

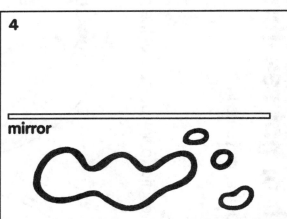

6

mirror

Draw your own shape here.

NO FUSS
PHOTOCOPIABLE

SCHOLASTIC
www.scholastic.co.uk

DANGER – Electricity!

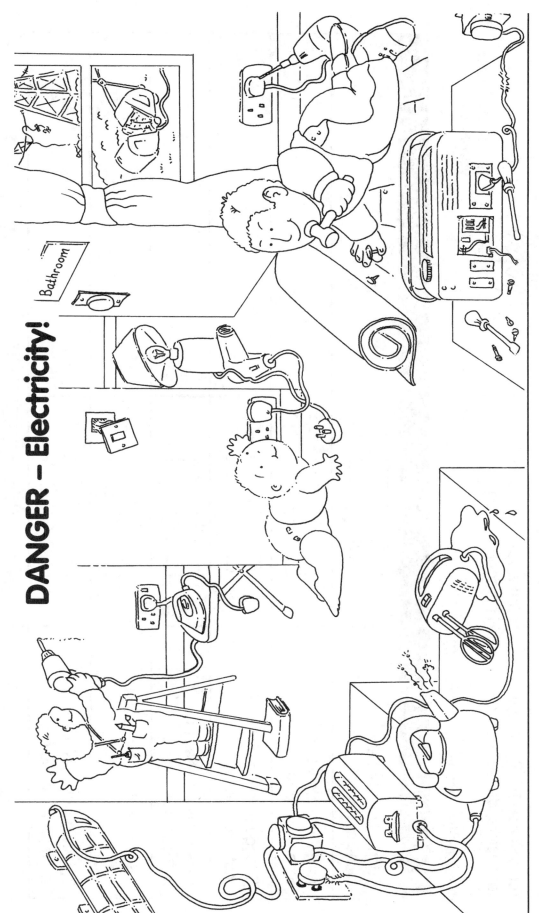

Electricity can be dangerous.
♣ Colour in red all the areas of danger in this picture.
♣ ♣ On the back of this sheet, explain why each area is dangerous and how the danger could be avoided.

Name _____

Electric motor

♣ Find out how an electric motor works in different circuits.

You will need: 1.5V battery, a bulb, some wires with crocodile connectors, an electric motor, a small cardboard circle.

♣ Fill in this observation table.

Fit a card wheel to your motor.

Circuit	Circuit diagram	Observations
Connect one battery to the motor.		
Turn the battery the other way round.		
Change over the motor terminals.		
Connect two batteries to the motor.		
Add one bulb to the circuit.		
With two batteries, include a short pencil in the circuit.		

NO FUSS
PHOTOCOPIABLE

SCHOLASTIC
www.scholastic.co.uk

Clown's face

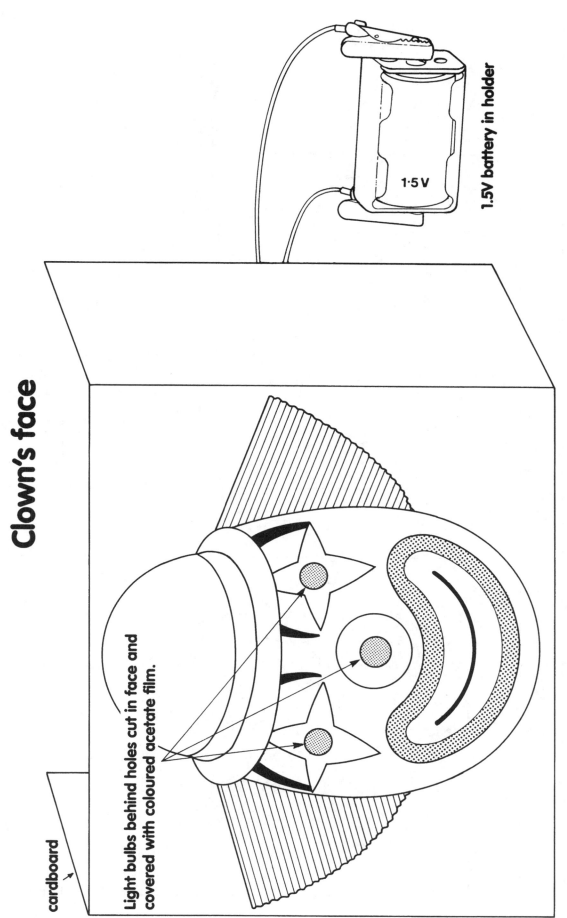

1·5V

1.5V battery in holder

cardboard

Light bulbs behind holes cut in face and covered with coloured acetate film.

✿ Can you make **all** the bulbs light up?
✿ Can you make the nose flash?

Wheel of fortune

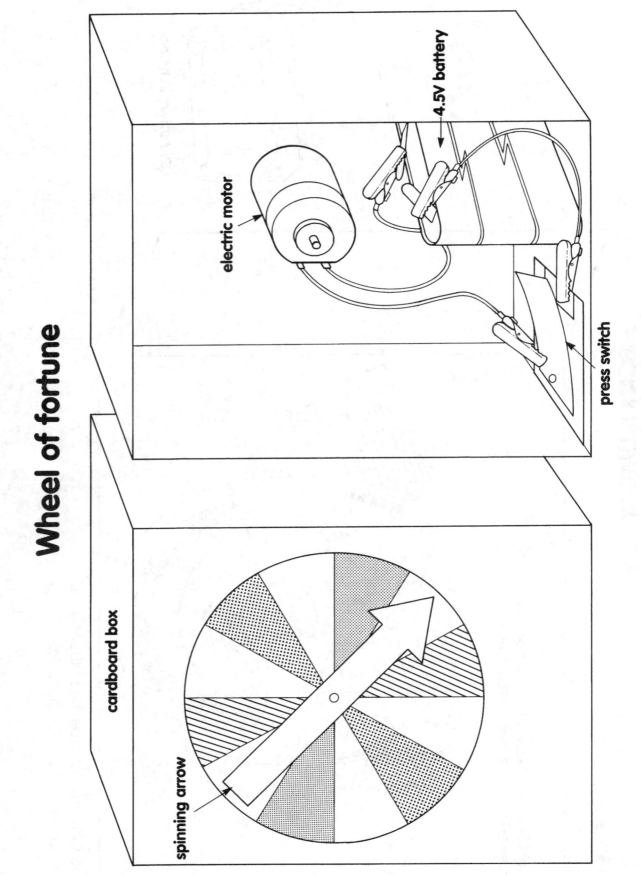

4.5V battery

electric motor

press switch

cardboard box

spinning arrow

NO FUSS PHOTOCOPIABLE

SCHOLASTIC
www.scholastic.co.uk

Name _____

Car-park barrier

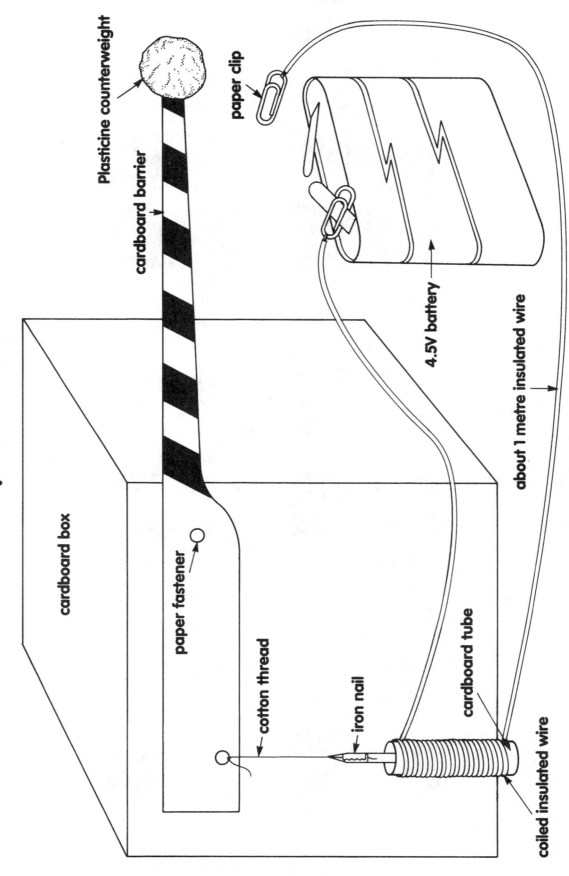

■ SCHOLASTIC

In this series:

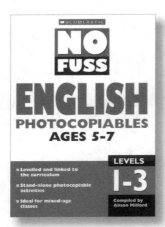

ISBN 0-439-96548-9
ISBN 978-0439-96548-4

ISBN 0-439-96549-7
ISBN 978-0439-96549-1

ISBN 0-439-96550-0
ISBN 978-0439-96550-7

ISBN 0-439-96551-9
ISBN 978-0439-96551-4

ISBN 0-439-96552-7
ISBN 978-0439-96552-1

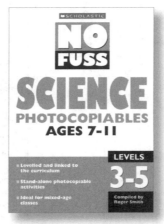

ISBN 0-439-96553-5
ISBN 978-0439-96553-8

To find out more, call: 0845 603 9091
or visit our website www.scholastic.co.uk